RADAR AND OTHER
ELECTRONIC INVENTIONS

ALSO BY FRANK ROSS, JR.

Young People's Book of Jet Propulsion

Guided Missiles

Ben Franklin, Scientist

Flying Windmills
    The Story of the Helicopter

Space Ships and Space Travel

RADAR AND OTHER
ELECTRONIC INVENTIONS

BY FRANK ROSS, JR.

NEW YORK

LOTHROP, LEE & SHEPARD CO., INC.

Library of Congress Catalog Card Number: 54-10296

Third Printing, September, 1961

Printed in the United States of America

To

Aloysius and Catherine

CONTENTS

CHAPTER

1 Electronics 1

2 Radar—Origin, Development and
   Operation 31

3 Radar Today 69

4 Electronics at Work 106

5 Versatile Electrons 171

6 Electronics and the Future 224

   Index 241

RADAR AND OTHER
ELECTRONIC INVENTIONS

ELECTRONICS

Historical Development

As a result of the scientific and technical advances taking place in our world today, we often hear that we are passing through the age of electricity, the chemistry age, or the age of aviation. More recent opinion has predicted the coming of the atomic age. All of these phrases have their vigorous supporters and all, to a very large extent, can be backed up with a considerable amount of proof. This leads to the suggestion that perhaps the most accurate expression would be "the age of technical and scientific versatility." In any event, any listing of the specialized "ages" in order of their importance would more than likely place the age of electricity at the top or very close to it.

Scientists of many lands and through many generations have devoted their lives to unraveling the mysteries of electrical matter. Their efforts have resulted not only in the accumulation of a vast amount of fundamental knowledge on electronics, but also in the development of a wide variety of machines and devices for putting that knowledge to work for the benefit of man. Today there is hardly a phase of daily living uninfluenced in some way by the wizardry of electricity or, more particularly, by one of its most fascinating branches, electronics.

As a product of electrical research, electronics is not very old, having been born just before the turn of the century. But some like to believe that its roots are much older, that it can be traced back to the times of the ancient Greeks and pinpointed in the work of Thales of Miletus.

Thales was a mathematician, astronomer and scientist all rolled into one. Because of a natural curiosity about the world in which he lived, he was the first, it is believed, to have observed the strange and powerful effects of electricity. His acquaintance with it stemmed from experiments with amber and silk. When he rubbed the two together, he noticed how the amber attracted thin pieces of wood and straw. Frictional electricity, which was what Thales was really toying with, soon became a popular subject for study and conversation. The Greeks, rarely at a loss in originating a word to fit a new situation or development, called the action which Thales had discovered *elektron*.

They derived this word from *elektor,* meaning "gleaming, the sun," because the amber used to produce frictional electricity has a bright sheen. Although our own word *electronics* stems from *elektron,* all resemblance between the two really stops there. As we shall see later, electronics as we know it today is a far cry from what it meant to the Greeks.

Thales' studies of the natural world occurred some time between 670 and 540 B.C. From the moment when he first revealed the magic force of electricity, scientists the world over and down through the centuries pursued its fascinating trail. But not until the mid-1800's did scientists really begin storming the many mysterious doors leading to a new science, a servant of mankind equal in importance to electricity, the science of electronics.

To tell of the work of those early scientists and how it led to the present-day age of electronics would take volumes. Since that is not the aim of this book, we shall discuss only those whose activity is closely related to our subject of electronics.

Few names in any account of the origin and development of electronics rank higher than that of Sir Joseph J. Thomson. This great English physicist devoted most of his scientific life to the study of electrical matter and he had many achievements to his credit. Of these, however, none surpasses his contribution in proving the actual existence of the basic component of electricity known as an electron. Thomson reached his conclusion in 1897, after long experiment and observation of the action of cathode rays, electrical discharges in a vacuum tube. The rays

2

at that time provided absorbing laboratory material to scientists of many lands. During the period of Thomson's research on cathode rays, scientists had differing opinions as to their real nature. Some firmly believed they were tiny particles of matter, while others were equally convinced that the rays were less substantial and compared them to light rays.

Thomson's experiments and mathematical analysis proved that the rays were made of material particles, but he went even further. He showed that the particles were of the tiniest size yet known to science. Up to that time, atoms had held this distinction. In addition, Thomson stated that regardless of where they were found, the relationship of physical mass to electrical charge was the same for these tiny bits of matter. At first Thomson called the infinitesimal components of the cathode ray *corpuscles*. Later the word was changed to *electron*, first used by another English physicist, G. Johnstone Stoney, in 1891, to describe a basic particle of electricity.

Proof of the electron's existence ushered in a new concept of the composition of physical matter which makes up the natural world. It served as a guiding light for later scientists who followed the long road to the wonderland of electronics.

Others whose names must be placed high on the roster of electronic pioneers were Sir William Crookes, Doctor Wilhelm Roentgen and Karl F. Braun. They, too, conducted long studies of cathode rays and especially of the tubes in which these rays were created. Crookes experimented with his cathode-ray tubes in 1878. These were based for the most part on those developed years previously by Heinrich Geissler, a German physicist. But the English scientist's tubes represented a great improvement because they contained a better vacuum.

Crookes' cathode-ray tubes were long glass cylinders within which a filament was fixed at one end. When the experimenter connected the tube to an electric current the filament became heated and shot off an electron beam. As long as there was any air within the tube, the electrons would cause it to glow. But

Some early forms of tubes that led to present day cathode-ray tube. Upper left center is one of the earliest developed by Heinrich Geissler in 1857. To its right is tube created by Karl F. Braun in 1898 in which stream of electrons was guided by magnetic control. Tube at left center with cross was made by Sir William Crookes in 1878. Conventional looking light bulb in center was used by Edison to discover his famous electronic "Effect." Tube to its right is similar to one developed by Lee De Forest in which he placed an electrically charged grid between the hot cathode and cold anode to regulate the flow of current. Sir Joseph J. Thompson in 1897 used tube like that in lower left corner for his experiments with an electron beam. *Allen B. Du Mont Laboratories, Inc.*

Crookes discovered that if the vacuum could be made high enough, the small amount of remaining air would not light up. Instead, a fluorescent spot of light would appear at the positive or opposite end of the tube. He further observed that if a metal object were fixed in the middle of the tube in the path of the electron beam, a shadow of that object would fall at the glowing end of the tube. This was proof to Crookes that whatever caused the glowing spot was moving in a straight line.

Like Sir Joseph Thomson, Crookes was extremely interested in the composition of cathode rays. Several years before their real nature was revealed, he had speculated that the mysterious stream of particles was made up of a "fourth state of matter." It remained for Thomson to prove the correctness of this theory.

When cathode-ray tubes first came into existence, scientists thought they had no practical value except for scientific research. But in 1895 something occurred to change that attitude. With the help of a cathode-ray tube, a German physicist, Doctor Wilhelm Konrad von Roentgen, made the now historic discovery of the X-ray. During the course of experimenting with this device in his laboratory one day, the scientist concealed it in a light-proof box. Then he darkened his workshop to check whether any light was escaping from the tube. To his surprise he noticed a glowing effect coming from a nearby object, a metal screen coated with a fluorescent chemical, barium platinocyanide. Roentgen suspected that his cathode tube was throwing off some kind of radiation rather than emitting light, but what it was he could not say. Thus he gave the name X-ray to the unknown radiation.

Before long Roentgen found that these X-rays affected sensitized photographic plates. Using his wife's hand as a subject, he had her place it on a photo-sensitive surface and then proceeded to aim the mysterious rays upon it. The bone structure of the hand was clearly outlined on the plate. Thus he had taken the world's first X-ray picture.

In 1898 the Crookes tube underwent drastic refinement at the hands of Karl Braun of Germany. Taking up the study of cathode rays where Crookes had left off, he produced a tube in which the beam of electrons could be guided. Braun accomplished this with a magnetic device which deflected the cathode ray and permitted it to trace patterns on a fluorescent screen. Actually this was the first real step toward today's television tube. Braun had come very close to creating a practical TV image receiver, lacking only a mechanism to control the spread of the electron beam which would be necessary before the lights and darks of an image could be projected on the face of a tube.

Aside from its application to television, Karl Braun's cathode-ray tube today serves many purposes in science and industrial activities. Little changed fundamentally from the one he developed, the device is now popularly known as a cathode-ray oscillograph.

Scientists during the early years of electronic research gave the cathode ray the lion's share of attention during their experimental investigations, as though sensing the important role it would some day play in electronics. How prophetic they were we well know today. Cathode rays play a vital part in radar operation, television transmisson, and, as we have already seen, as a research and test instrument in the form of the oscillograph.

Another of the early giants of the electrical world was Thomas Edison. He is chiefly known, of course, for his electrical and mechanical inventions. However, his laboratory discovery known as the "Edison Effect," though not so famous, has had a profound influence on the development of electronics, particularly during its pioneering years. The "Edison Effect," which concerned the odd behavior of electric current, first attracted attention during a tedious laboratory session aimed at improving the quality of the newborn incandescent light bulb.

At that time the bulb was far from its present state of perfection. One of its weaknesses was a tendency to turn black, especially toward the end of its life. Edison and his assistants

6

had come to the conclusion that the black coating was caused by the carbon filaments used in light bulbs. As the filaments became heated, black carbon particles broke loose and flowed toward the glass surface. By placing a third filament between the two already inside the bulb, they thought, they might prevent the formation of the carbon film. Connecting the third filament to a lamp circuit, they allowed electric current to pass through the first filament. Then something strange happened. The third filament, though not connected to the original two, became eletcrified and passed current back through the circuit which Edison had constructed.

How did the third filament become electrified? At first the men were puzzled. Further experiments showed that if the third filament was hooked up to the negative side of the circuit, this flow of current would not take place. It seemed to be strictly a one-way affair. This mysterious electrical behavior, due to moving electrons, was only understood years later. As the original filaments became heated, electrons were released and flashed across the gap to the third filament. This stream of electrical matter energized the new filament. The fact that electrons only move from a hot source to a cold one accounted for their one-way journey.

This unusual electronic action had little to do with the eventual improvement of the incandescent bulb. Many believe, however, that it provided one of the more important links in the complex structure of electronics as it exists today.

A more immediate result of these experiments was the granting of a patent to Edison, on October 21, 1884, for a governor device, based on the "Edison Effect," to regulate the output of electrical generators. Although the device was not effective, mainly because the existing tubes had poor vacuums, the patent is believed to have been the first issued in the field of electronics.

When Edison and his laboratory aids came upon this strange one-way action of electrical current, they were much too concerned with other projects to realize the full importance of

Thomas Edison with three of his early electric light bulbs with which he discovered and studied what is now called the "Edison Effect." *Thomas Alva Edison Foundation, Inc.*

their discovery. It remained for other scientists, notably Sir Ambrose Fleming and Lee De Forest, to adapt the "Edison Effect" to more valuable and historic electronic devices. Fleming, an English physicist, used the "Edison Effect" to invent the first electronic tube for detecting wireless waves. He had long been engaged in electrical experiments and, after becoming acquainted with Edison's discovery, followed it up with many investigations of his own.

Fleming's research career reached its peak at the beginning of this century when wireless telegraphy was extremely new. Though even then looked upon as almost one of the world's wonders, it was in need of considerable improvement. The device, for example, for picking up wireless signals, called a coherer, was very unreliable and something better was definitely needed. The coherer, invented by a French scientist, Edouard Branly, was a glass tube containing particles of iron. The tube was hooked up in an electric circuit with a galvanometer and a battery. As a radio signal coursed through the antenna of a wireless receiver to the coherer, the iron particles

8

would unify or cohere. When this occurred, the coherer became a conductor for the battery current, which in turn operated a telephone bell or telegraph key.

To prevent the coherer from becoming a conductor, it had to be struck lightly with a hammer-like instrument which was part of the coherer apparatus. The shock scattered the iron filings, thus breaking off the current. This action took place automatically in the telegraph set after a radio signal was received. As a result, the dot-and-dash pattern of the incoming signals was duplicated by the battery current operating the telegraph key.

Many scientists had been working on the problem of a better wireless signal detector, among them Fleming, then consultant to the Marconi Wireless Telegraph Company. By using the "Edison Effect" in a tube with a double set of filaments, he developed his famous electronic detector tube. He called it an oscillator valve. Soon it became known as the Fleming valve, and later as a diode tube. What Fleming's invention accomplished was to change alternating current in wireless apparatus into pulsating direct current of sufficient strength to operate a bell or a telegraph key.

Alternating current travels in one direction, then reverses itself. It is positive flowing one way, and negative in the other. As such, it is useless for telegraphy and must be changed or rectified into a direct current moving only in one path. When Fleming's electronic valve controlled the flow of electricity in the positive direction, the telegraph equipment could be operated. But when the negative force was flowing, the telegraph receiver stopped working.

Fleming secured a patent on his invention in 1905. Recognized as a vast improvement over the older methods for picking up wireless signals, the tube soon won acceptance.

The introduction of Fleming's device stimulated the thinking of many scientists throughout the world, but none more so than that of Dr. Lee De Forest of the United States. Using both the

"Edison Effect" and Fleming's tube as a starting point for his own experiments, De Forest developed the "audion" electronic tube, which was capable of converting weak radio signals into sound. This ushered in the era of radio broadcasting.

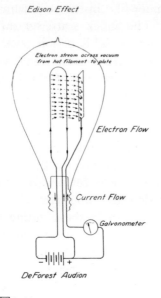

Edison Effect

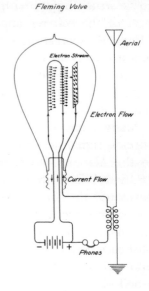

Fleming Valve

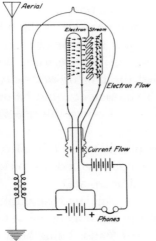

DeForest Audion

Three early electronic accomplishments that did so much to launch successfully the science of electronics as we know it today. Reprinted by permission from *The Edison Effect* by Vice Admiral Harold G. Bowen, page 24, published by the *Thomas Alva Edison Foundation, Inc.*, copyright, 1951.

Between the two sets of filaments in Fleming's detector tube, De Forest placed a third element. This consisted of a piece of platinum wire bent zigzag, which he called a grid. Hooked up to a proper electrical circuit, he found, the three-electrode vacuum tube could not only pick up radio impulses but could generate and amplify them as well. One of De Forest's associates, Clifford Babcock, is said to have suggested the name "audion" for the new tube and was responsible for placing the detecting and generating elements inside a glass shield in which a vacuum existed.

De Forest made his comparatively simple invention in 1906. By adding a third electrode in the electron stream flowing between the first and second filaments of a vacuum tube, thus regulating its flow still further, he turned the wireless world upside down. Within a few short years his tube eliminated the old arcing method of generating wireless waves, but perhaps even more important, it established the groundwork for radio transmission.

De Forest himself gave one of the earliest demonstrations in this new communication field on January 13, 1910. He set up a broadcasting set backstage at the Metropolitan Opera House in New York City and sent out over the air waves, for the first time, the world-famous singing voice of Enrico Caruso and others of the opera company. Scientists and engineers have since developed innumerable variations of the grid-vacuum tube along with complicated circuits which can perform countless wonders for the benefit of man. Indeed, De Forest's electronic invention can truly be called the key that opened the door to the magical world of electrical devices and systems which we know today as electronics.

The Electron

In order to understand more easily the vast, complicated field of electronics in its present expanded scope, it is helpful to know something of the physical characteristics of the electron.

11

Since the time of Crookes and Thomson, when the infinitely small particle of matter was first recognized, scientists the world over have found out many things about it. Let us see what a few of these are.

Most of us are familiar with the fact that all matter, whether liquids, solids, or gases, is made up of molecules. These, we are told, are the smallest physical portions of which substances consist. Molecules, however, are themselves made up of still tinier components known as atoms. Atoms, according to physicists, are the building blocks of our physical world. So far 92 different natural atomic elements—those found in the earth and atmosphere of the world—are known to exist. Eight others have been created in the laboratory. The lightest element is hydrogen, which is identified by the atomic number one. Atoms are extraordinarily small and often very complicated in their make-up. They are powerhouses of energy. Scientists tell us that atoms have a diameter of about one-hundred-millionth of an inch. It remained for the scientific investigation of a Danish physicist by the name of Niels Bohr to give us one of the earliest theoretical pictures of the atom in 1913.

Bohr believed that the atom was made up of a comparatively stable nucleus consisting of positive charges of electrical matter

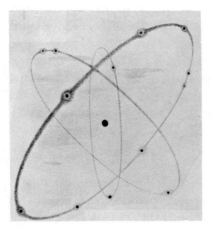

Electrons spinning in their orbits around the nucleus of an atom. *Allen B. Du Mont Laboratories, Inc.*

called protons. Spinning about the nucleus on various orbital levels, much like the planets around the sun, are still other tiny particles of electrical matter called electrons. These are electrically negative in nature. Protons and electrons in a well-behaved atom tend to neutralize one another. That is, there are the same number of electrons as protons. Atoms are, therefore, normally neutral in nature but, if by some means they are made to lose one of their electrons, they are said to be positive in nature because the protons outnumber the electrons. Atoms become negative, of course, when one of the protons is lost and the electrons are in the majority.

More recently physicists discovered that some electrons may have a positive charge. To distinguish these from negative electrons, they are called positrons. Technically, then, electrons can be both positive and negative. However, because of the great difficulty in isolating positrons, scientists know little about them. For the purposes of this story we shall deal only with the negative members of the family.

Electrons are so tiny in nature that no man has ever seen one. Yet scientists have succeeded in isolating and measuring them. They tell us that about 29 billion billion billion electrons would probably be needed to weigh an ounce! In diameter the electron is said to be on the scale of one-six-trillionth of an inch. The groundwork of electronic research lies in freeing electrons from their atoms, usually those in the outermost shells surrounding the nucleus, and controlling them for various purposes. Over the past decade or two scientists have become so absorbed with the atom's nucleus of protons; and electrons that they have created an entirely new branch of physics called nucleonics, through which they discovered the secret of releasing atomic energy. Having mastered this power, they are now busily engaged in finding ways to control it for the betterment of mankind.

There are a number of techniques for releasing electrons from atoms to achieve a wide variety of results. The most important method is by heat, or in the technical phrase, "thermionic emission." This impressive phrase simply means that if a metal substance, such as the filament in a lamp, is heated to the required temperature, electrons will break loose from their atoms and stream off into space. Edison, as we have pointed out, was one of the first to notice this. Another method is by exposure to a light beam or a particular type of electromagnetic radiation, as with photoelectric tubes. Then we have a technique called secondary emission, in which one group of electrons bombards a second group. For every electron that strikes a target, one or many electrons may fly off from the impact. A somewhat similar method involves a head-on crash between an electron particle and a gas molecule. As a result of the collision, the molecule gives up an electron and becomes electrified, positive in character. Still another method utilizes a powerful electrical force applied to metals. This is known as field emission. Finally, electrons are freed when radioactive substances release their pent-up energy.

As we have already mentioned, electrons in atoms move in orbits of various levels around a nucleus. Physicists refer to these different orbital levels as shells. Each shell may have one or several electrons speeding in its spherical path. A copper atom, for example, has two electrons whirling about in one shell, eight in another, eighteen in a third, and one in a fourth. The total of 29 equals the number of positive proton charges. Electrons keep constantly on the move, never resting.

When the electrons of a particular atom are influenced by an inner or outer force, they can be made to move from one shell or energy level to the next. If the force is great enough, they may even leave their atom entirely for another, thus permitting electricity to flow between them. One kind of electronic action through which this occurs is called ionization. This process may cause neutral atoms to lose or pick up one or more electrons, becoming electrified particles, and turning positive or negative

14

in nature as the case may be. Ionization usually takes place when electrical energy is passed through gas-filled tubes or other containers holding solutions capable of conducting electricity.

Electrons spinning around in the outermost shells of an atom are normally less firmly held in place when affected by another source of energy. Those traveling along the inner spherical paths are harder to move. Electrons are more easily set free by some substances than others, both in quantity and speed of movement. These are usually known as free electrons. Heat, certain types of rays, and even light are sufficient to release these electrons. Metal substances in which electrons can move swiftly and easily from one atom to another are said to be good electrical conductors. Copper and aluminum are two such metals. Certain liquids, called electrolytes, made of acids or salts, are also excellent conductors.

On the other hand, another family of solid substances follows exactly the opposite behavior, giving up electrons very sparingly or not at all. In these substances, the electrons remain tightly bound to their nucleus and do not skip freely to neighboring atoms. These are known as non-conductors of electrical energy, such as glass, rubber materials, ceramics, and mica. To those who work in the electrical field, these non-conducting materials are also referred to as dielectrics. Perhaps contrary to what one might expect, these substances do have an important place in the electronics field. They are used to block off or slow down the movement of electrical current, and are identified in this application by still a third name, insulators. Of course, non-conducting materials also provide important elements in the construction of electronic tubes.

The ability to release electrons from their atoms and control their movement through a vacuum or gas-filled tube has enabled scientists to harness them for myriad jobs. And dozens of different types of vacuum or gas-filled tubes constitute the chief medium for applying the versatility of electronic energy.

Electronic Tubes

Present-day electronic tubes include the common vacuum tube, phototube, gas-filled tube, and the extremely important cathode-ray tube. Basically they are alike in that they consist of a cathode, which is the source for electrons, and one or more anodes, usually the objectives toward which the electrons move. Some tubes utilize anodes for guiding and controlling the passage of electricity. These elements are fixed inside a container from which the air has been partly or completely removed. The vacuum condition permits the electrons to move with greater ease than if air were present.

Scientists have found that if they coat the cathode with certain chemical elements like barium or calcium, it will increase the output of electrons. Ordinarily the production of electrons from a cathode is governed by its temperature and by the kind of material of which it is made. Cathodes coated with oxides are commonly used in radio and television receivers. Tubes designed to handle great quantities of electrical power have cathodes made of pure tungsten metal, which outlasts other materials under the tremendously high temperatures involved. X-ray tubes usually employ cathodes of this type. Tungsten cathodes may be made of round or rectangular-shaped wire and twisted into countless forms, spirals, hairpin curves, and even the letter M.

The anode, the second major element of an electronic tube, is also of metal, but its requirements are not as demanding as those for the cathode. Nickel and its alloys, iron and tantalum are most commonly used. One of the most important functions of the material of an anode is to radiate heat. For this reason the material is often impregnated with graphite. Anodes are usually made in rectangular or cylindrical shapes and slipped over the cathode.

The simplest type of electronic tube, nothing more than a refinement of the one Edison used to obtain his famous "Effect" and Fleming to invent his oscillator, is called the diode. This

A TYPICAL SUBMINIATURE TRIODE
Structure of a Typical Miniature Tube.

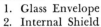

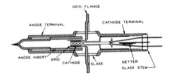

1. Glass Envelope
2. Internal Shield
3. Plate
4. Grid No. 3 (Suppressor)
5. Grid No. 2 (Screen)
6. Grid No. 1 (Control Grid)
7. Cathode
8. Heater
9. Exhaust Tip
10. Getter
11. Spacer Shield Header
12. Insulating Spacer
13. Spacer Shield
14. Inter-Pin Shield
15. Glass Button-Stem Shield
16. Lead Wire
17. Base Pin
18. Glass-to-Metal Seal
Radio Corporation of America

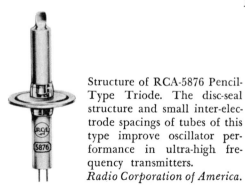

Exhaust tube

Envelope Assembly

Structure of RCA-5876 Pencil-Type Triode. The disc-seal structure and small inter-electrode spacings of tubes of this type improve oscillator performance in ultra-high frequency transmitters.
Radio Corporation of America.

Grid

Cathode Assembly

Heater-and-Getter Assembly

The giant tube is a super-power beam triode capable of providing an output of 500,000 watts. It weighs 135 pounds and is 38¾″ long. The young lady is holding a tiny phototube ¼″ in diameter and 1-11/32″ long. *Radio Corporation of America.*

tube is made of one cathode and one anode. In the diode tube current can flow in only one direction. It has proved an excellent device for changing alternating electrical current into direct current, which accounts for the name of "rectifier tube." Diodes can be either gas-filled or of the vacuum type. Gas-filled diodes are frequently found in chargers, used to restore life to weak storage batteries, and in certain other industrial equipment where direct current is needed for electroplating processes.

The next basic kind of electron tube, known as the triode, owes its existence to the work of Dr. Lee De Forest. By inserting a grid element in the electron stream, he provided a control device. When negative in nature, the grid slows down the flow of electrons to the anode. When positive, it speeds up the flow. Triode-tube grids are delicate units of construction usually made of fine nickel wire. This is wound in the shape of a helix and made rigid by vertical pieces of wire to which it is fastened. The grid is carefully placed between the cathode and anode, usually in such a way as to completely hide the former. Because

18

of their extremely important ability to amplify radio signals, triodes come in a wide range of types and sizes, measuring from one inch all the way to nine feet. Some of the triode types developed for special electronic tasks are called Pentodes, Tetrodes, Beam-Power tubes, and the like.

One of the best known of all electronic tubes, especially since the introduction in recent years of radar and television, is the cathode-ray tube. In point of years, the cathode-ray tube is probably the oldest member in the electronics tube field.

This cathode ray tube is typical of those used in an oscilloscope. *Radio Corporation of America.*

Heinrich Geissler, a German physicist, produced and experimented with some of the first cathode-ray tubes in the mid-1800's. His vacuum tubes were long, thin glass devices with electrodes fixed inside at both ends. As he directed current through the electrodes, the residue of air within the tube began to glow. Crookes, Braun, and others all contributed their bit toward making the tube more effective.

But only in more recent times, with the general advancement of the whole science of electronics, has the cathode-ray tube achieved some of the wonderful things of which it is capable.

Almost everyone who owns a television receiver is familiar with the general shape of a cathode-ray tube. One end of the

19

tube has a thin neck, while the other flares out to a large rectangular area. This contains the surface or face of the tube and shows in visual form the electronic impulses streaming from the cathode. The cathode tube is essentially made up of three main parts: the electron gun, a fluorescent screen which also serves as an anode, and the electron-gun control.

The electron gun has a cathode which, when heated properly, sends off a stream of electrons. The electron generator releases the particles in just one direction. A metal grid fits over the cathode, where it serves two purposes instead of one as at other times. Besides controlling the intensity of the electron beam (flow of electrons), the grid, by means of a tiny hole in its top, focuses the beam into a narrow stream of electrons. Some cathode-ray tubes have one anode, some two, depending on the type of beam control that is used. The beam control may be a magnetic or electrical coil device or a combination of the two circling the neck of the tube. It can deflect the stream of electrons up, down, and from side to side.

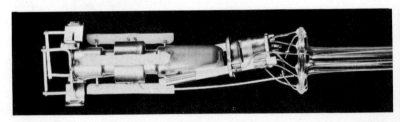

View of a typical cathode ray gun. Electron beam shoots out of right side. *Allen B. Du Mont Laboratories, Inc.*

The funnel-shaped interior at the wide end of the tube leading up to the face is treated with a special coating which transforms it into an anode with a strong positive charge. This helps speed up the beam of electrons as they travel to the face of the tube. The anode also carries off secondary electrons freed after the beam strikes the fluorescent screen.

The inner face of the cathode tube on which the beam of electrons falls is coated with phosphor substances. Electrons striking phosphor will produce light. A TV tube may have its face covered with a mixture of zinc sulphide, which produces a light that is almost white in color. This is what we commonly see on our home TV receivers. Cathode tubes used in certain electronic testing or measuring devices like the oscillograph are coated with willemite, which causes the beam to show up as a green light. Sometimes phosphors are applied to create special effects such as a bluish light when the visual results on a cathode screen are to be photographed.

Dr. Vladimir K. Zworykin, an American scientist, was one of the principal figures who helped perfect the cathode-ray tube for television. Picking up the electronic trail from others, such as Karl Braun, Dr. Zworykin improved the electron-gun portion of the cathode tube to the point where it could successfully paint images on a fluorescent screen. He also invented a cathode-ray tube called the iconoscope, for use in a television camera, capable of viewing images and flashing them out over the air waves. Later we shall see how this device works along with other elements of TV operation.

The cathode-ray tube is not only important to television and the oscillograph, but also to those other marvels of electronics, radar, and the electronic microscope. In addition, it has led to

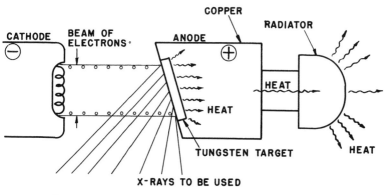

FUNDAMENTALS OF AN X-RAY TUBE

General Electric X-Ray Corp.

21

the development of the X-ray tube, which has become one of the most important weapons used by the medical world to combat the ills of mankind. The value of X-rays for medical purposes became apparent shortly after Roentgen announced his discovery and special tubes were created to produce them.

Many of the early X-ray tubes consisted of a cathode and anode along with a small amount of gas sealed inside a glass container. The cathode was a concave disc of aluminum. A block of copper coated with platinum served as the anode, so placed that when the stream of electrons struck it, X-rays flashed from the target. The amount of gas within the tube determined its characteristics. With a relatively large quantity, the tube would produce "soft" X-rays of low penetrating power. On the other hand, if the vacuum were higher, "hard" X-rays with high penetrating strength were created.

To control these characteristics, some of the early X-ray tubes had a second tube in which gas could be generated to lower the vacuum in the main tube. Varying the voltage between the cathode and anode also affected the tube's working ability.

Since doctors wanted X-rays of varying degrees of penetration, they would often acquire an assortment of tubes. This arrangement did not produce good results. Further, early X-ray tubes were not easy to adjust. An American physicist, Dr. William D. Coolidge, experimented with these X-ray generators and made them far more effective, leading up to the models now in existence.

Dr. Coolidge altered the tube by using a hot tungsten filament instead of a cold aluminum disc to produce the electron stream. The temperature of the filament could be controlled by a simple rheostat. This in turn determined the velocity of the electrons streaming from the cathode which governed the characteristics of the tube's X-rays. All this took place inside a glass shield containing the highest possible vacuum attainable. Tubes built according to Dr. Coolidge's ideas could produce X-rays of varying penetrating power and were extremely stable.

There exist today many types of X-ray tubes. But despite differences in their outward appearance or the kind of work they do, they are basically of the diode class with a high vacuum. X-ray tubes, particularly very powerful ones, use only a small percentage of their energy for the actual production of penetrating rays, releasing the major portion in the form of heat. For this reason the tubes are equipped with special cooling devices. Some are encased in containers and cooled by circulating water. Others have metal fins sticking out from their cylindrical surface so the heat may be carried away by air. A third method involves the immersion of the tube in a pool of oil. This is used most often with powerful X-ray apparatus which can generate 2,000,000 and more volts. Tubes employed in this equipment are truly complicated devices which can shoot out X-rays of great penetrating power.

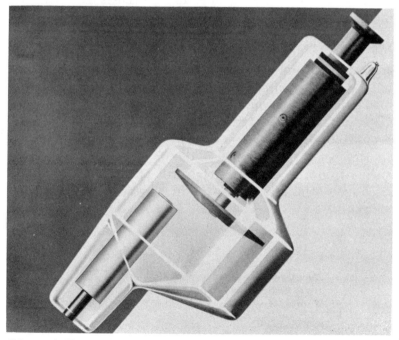

Diagnostic X-ray tubes and drawing of typical control panel. *General Electric Co.*

Million-volt multi-section X-ray tube of the kind used in medicine and industry. *General Electric Co.*

The vacuum electronic tubes mentioned so far are by no means the only ones in that family. There are many others with technical names like Klystron, Magnetron—used for high-frequency transmissions—and Cyclotron and Resnatron, each with its own specialized tasks for the production and control of electromagnetic waves.

Electronic tubes of the gas-filled family are usually made to hold a gas of a non-active nature. The gas causes the electrodes to act differently from the ordinary high-vacuum types. The gases most frequently employed with these tubes may be mercury vapor, xenon, argon, and hydrogen. Scientists and engineers have found that tubes of this kind can perform many valuable tasks in electronics which the conventional vacuum tubes cannot. Their widest application is in the field of electric power, such as switching devices in powerline circuits. They are also used for illumination in homes, factories, and other places. The number of tube varieties in this group is also rather large, ranging from the comparatively small photo flash bulb with which most of us are familiar, to the Thyratron, Excitron and Ignitron.

This tiny electron tube belongs to the vacuum phototube family. *Radio Corporation of America.*

Photoelectric tubes are probably the most uncanny of all such sources of electronic power. They merely have to be struck by a visible light ray to release their electrons. These light-sensitive tubes, also known as phototubes, perform a wide number of jobs ranging from the best-known, the automatic opening of doors, to a whole host of industrial activities. The television and motion picture industries, for example, rely heavily on many different types of photoelectric tubes.

These tubes do not differ too greatly from others. Most frequently gas-filled, though sometimes of the vacuum variety, they have the usual two electrodes sealed within a glass shield. The cathode is often in the form of a curved shield, which has been found most effective for passing electrons to the anode. The anode is merely a rod rising up through the center of the tube. Silver or nickel usually serves as the base metal for the cathode and this is coated with a special substance whose electrons are in a highly fluid state. Titanium, potassium, thorium and cesium are commonly used since they easily release their electrons when struck by light or other radiant energy rays. Pholoelectric tubes, or cells, as they are sometimes called, are also sensitive to invisible days or "dark light." Body heat, for example, is usually sufficient to set the tubes in action. Many types of burglar-alarm systems are based on this characteristic of phototubes.

Electromagnetic Waves

Perhaps some of the earliest fundamental contributions to the understanding of electromagnetic waves were those of James Clerk Maxwell, a well-known nineteenth-century scientist. He believed that the electrical charges and magnetic forces of which they were made moved through space with wave-like motions and with the speed of light. He also established a mathematical basis for the study of electromagnetic forces. Scientists today, though still somewhat puzzled by these electrical phenomena, have made some progress in ferreting out the answers.

For example, they know that when electromagnetic waves travel through space, they move in a circular pattern much like a compressed coiled spring when suddenly released, and with the speed of light rays—186,000 miles per second. Indeed, electromagnetic waves have many other features of light. They can be reflected, refracted and diffracted. Structurally, it is believed, they are movements of electrical and magnetic fields made up of atomic particles. Their swift, continuing motion results in the release of energy.

Scientists have established a number of characteristics in electromagnetic waves, especially in regard to their length. For this reason they have classified them in spectrum form, which places them in order of length. A wavelength is measured as the distance separating the peak of one wave from that of the one following, similar to the space between the crests of sea waves. It is also the distance a wave travels through one complete frequency cycle. The length of electromagnetic waves can be varied by both the type of equipment employed to create them and the amount of power used. Their frequency is measured by the number of times a second they complete a cycle. To complete a cycle, an electric force must travel from zero strength to its maximum, then back to zero and again to maximum, and finally return to zero. Low frequencies produce "long" electromagnetic waves, high frequencies create "short" ones.

At one end of the electromagnetic spectrum, waves move at a comparatively slow speed and the distance between their peaks is estimated as about 6,000 miles. The movement or vibration of these slow-moving waves is something like 30 times a second or, as electronic engineers say, 30 cycles. The wavelengths of conventional "long" wave radio transmission range between 700 and 2,000 feet. At the other extreme of the electromagnetic scale of wavelengths and frequency we find a staggering contrast. The gap separating the peaks of these "short" waves measures something like one ten-thousandth of an angstrom, a technical term for the incredibly small space dividing the crests of these wavelengths. In numerical terms it equals about two-hundred-and-fifty-millionths of an inch. These waves can be made to occur on the high end of the spectrum more than thirty thousand quintillion times per second.

Electromagnetic waves ranging between 4,000 and 7,800 angstroms can be seen in the form of colored light days. This band of waves runs the gamut in colored shading from deep purple to deep red. Electromagnetic waves beyond the red limits, and for some distance thereafter, are felt as radiant heat. Those beyond the purple end are known as ultraviolet rays, with which we are all familiar for their ability to tan or burn the skin.

Another and very important band of specific electromagnetic waves occurs between 7,800 and about 1,500,000 angstroms. These waves begin where the red end of the visible spectrum disappears and extend without interruption to the ultra-short radio wave region. They are better known as infra-red rays and are heat producing. They can be studied and measured by sensitive heat-detecting instruments such as the bolometer and the spectro-bolometer. Much of the infra-red region can be photographed with special plates. As we shall see later, infra-red radiation serves important needs not only in industry but in the medical field as well.

We come now to still another band of electromagnetic waves, known as microwaves. These are very high up on the electromagnetic scale, almost in the region of the infra-red rays. At times microwaves can be seen and felt. Extremely short, they occur with great rapidity. One of the unusual qualities about these waves is that they can be focused like the beam of a searchlight to travel in a straight line, a characteristic which has made them highly valuable in radar and other means of communication. The distance between the peaks of microwaves is said to be only a fraction of an inch.

Another of their oddities is that they do not travel through solids, the way ordinary electric current does through wire.

Therefore, wires cannot transmit microwaves from one point to another in electronic equipment. One way engineers have overcome this problem is with wave guides. These pipe-like devices, round, square, or rectangular in cross-section, function somewhat like the voice-carrying speaking tube. Wave guides are precisely made, and their interior dimensions have an important relation to the particular band of microwaves that travels through them. They are an essential part of radar equipment.

One of the best-known of all electromagnetic waves is the one we call X-ray. At some time or other we have all read or heard about these rays, or even been exposed to them. We have previously discussed the discovery of these rays and how they are produced. Now we shall examine a few of their characteristics.

The X-ray band in the electromagnetic spectrum lies far beyond that of ultra-violet light. The rays are produced at a very high frequency and therefore have extremely short wavelengths. If we can imagine activity in terms of figures, the frequency of X-rays is estimated at from 2,000 trillion times a second to more than 100,000 quadrillion times a second! Wavelengths of X-rays can be varied. By controlling the amount of voltage behind the electron stream within the tube, some waves can be made long and some short. Long, low-frequency wavelengths give us the "soft" X-rays we have described earlier, which can hardly penetrate glass. With high-frequency, short wavelengths, on the other hand, we get the "hard" X-rays, which can go through metal inches thick.

X-rays, though not visible to the human eye, can be detected by chemicals and also by electrical devices. For example, if a screen were coated with barium platinocyanide, and X-rays directed at it, a vivid fluorescence would result. When a person stands between the chemically treated screen and the X-ray tube, the penetrating rays outline on the screen the internal portions of the body. Since bones and other solid parts of the human body do not permit the transmission of X-rays as readily as the softer portions, they show up much darker on the fluorescent screen. The same thing occurs when X-rays pass through the human body to strike a photographic plate.

Ultrasonics

A slight detour from electronics as such brings us to the subject of ultrasonics, the study of sound waves far above the range of human hearing. This extremely modern branch of science has so much in common with electronics that it rightfully belongs, however briefly, in any story on electronics. In fact, many of the current devices for creating ultrasonic sound waves are of an electronic nature.

When sound waves are produced with a frequency of about 18,000 times a second—18 kilocycles—they have just about reached the limits within which the human ear can pick up the noise. If the frequency is increased to 20 kilocycles or more, then the human ear can no longer detect sound vibrations. Sound waves in this super-noise region have numerous strange characteristics which have intrigued scientists. Many of these still remain a mystery, while some have been classified and applied to a number of different tasks, particularly where electrical energy cannot be utilized exclusively.

Some ranges in the ultrasonic region can be produced by mechanical means. But those that are in the very high bands must be created by electronic equipment. Sound waves of the ultrasonic variety are very similar to electromagnetic waves in that they can be radiated outward from the source like a beam of light. And, again, like electrical waves, if they strike an object, they reflect back to the point from which they came. A peculiar feature of ultrasonic waves is that they travel poorly through the air but quite well in water, which made them especially valuable in the creation of underwater sound-detecting equipment during World War II.

The name given to this wartime equipment, which the Allies employed for detecting German submarines, was SONAR—for sounding and ranging. An electronic unit was used in SONAR equipment for generating ultrasonic sound waves. This sound generator, usually fastened to the outside of the ship's hull under the waterline, contained special electronic tubes called strobotrons, which controlled the length of time of the sound impulses and their frequency. When directed beneath the sea, if they struck an object, they would bound back to a receiver aboard the vessel carrying SONAR.

By timing the returning echo, an operator at the receiving set could tell the depth and position of the detected underwater object. Since the end of World War II, scientists have continued their research in ultrasonics, so that now they have gathered enough knowledge to adapt it for civilian purposes as well as military.

CHAPTER TWO

RADAR—ORIGIN, DEVELOPMENT
AND OPERATION

Origin

If we were asked to select a particularly outstanding accomplishment in electronics, radar would come to mind as one of its more interesting examples. This electronic equipment with its invisible, magical rays that can "see" through clouds, fog, the blackness of night and beyond visual range, had achieved laboratory success several years before the outbreak of World War II. But the frenzied demands for new fighting tools during that conflict rushed it out of the experimental stage and into the realm of everyday use far sooner than would have happened through conventional research methods.

Unlike so many older important scientific inventions, radar cannot be credited to the research of a particular man or country. Its development into a practical device for varied uses represents the climax of a long story that goes back to the middle of the nineteenth century, embracing many countries and the patient, painstaking work of numerous scientists and engineers.

However, we can trace some important groundwork for the ultimate idea of radar to the electrical research, during the 1880's of Heinrich Hertz. Around that time, as we already know, Thomson, Crookes, Braun, Edison, and others were conducting an intensive campaign to solve many electrical and electronic mysteries. Hertz, investigating the properties of electromagnetic waves, discovered among other things that they could be reflected, just like light rays striking a shiny object. This is the heart of the principle on which radar operation is based.

Born in Germany, Hertz was a brilliant physicist. Although he died at thirty-seven, Hertz had already completed many far-reaching experiments which actually laid the basis for wireless

31

and radio as well as more modern radar. In his work with electromagnetic waves, Hertz employed extremely simple equipment. To produce these waves he used an oscillator, which he preferred to call an excitor, made of two small zinc plates, a pair of short brass rods with highly polished knobs at the ends, having a spark gap and an induction coil, along with several other parts. This elementary device enabled him to produce, for the first time, electrical waves of extremely short length.

Hertz used another simple piece of laboratory equipment for detecting ultra-short magnetic waves. This was a small length of copper wire which he bent into a circle. The ends of the wire were fitted with metal balls. The scientist would place the detector a short distance from the excitor. As the miniature transmitter sent out its electric waves, sparks would leap from the gap between the balls of the detector. Having produced and detected the presence of electromagnetic waves, Hertz went on to analyze their nature. One of the first things he discovered was their ability to be reflected from flat or curved metal surfaces. According to Hertz, this unusual occurrence was based on the same laws which caused the reflection of light waves. Another action of ultra-short waves which he found related to the laws of light was the speed with which they moved through the air.

By extensive mathematical calculations, he measured the length of electromagnetic waves, figured out the frequency with which they were sent out by the transmitter, and determined that their velocity was the same as that of a light wave, 186,000 miles a second. This particular trait of electromagnetic waves, in addition to their reflecting ability, of course, gives radar its great practical value. Actually Hertz provided laboratory proof for many of the electromagnetic-wave theories of James Clerk Maxwell.

Conceivably men like Crookes, Braun, Hertz, and other scientists busy with their fundamental electrical researches, might have envisioned the creation of some such apparatus as

32

radar through their work. The fact that they did not actually blueprint this device, even though they pioneered radar's essentials, is certainly no reflection on their mental ability or vision. After all, we must remember that at the time wireless was only in its infancy, while radio had not been invented. It remained for engineers and scientists of later years, studying the electrical discoveries of their predecessors, to advance ideas on the possibility of radar and even to predict its coming. Scientists like the amazing Nikola Tesla, for example, and the world-famous Guglielmo Marconi were among the foremost of these.

Among his associates in the world of electrical matters, Tesla was looked upon both as a genius and an impractical visionary. He was born in Yugoslavia, received a solid schooling in mathematics, physics and practical mechanical work, and later specialized in electrical engineering. At the age of twenty-seven, he decided that his future lay in America where, just before the turn of the century, progress in electrical science was moving ahead at a rapid pace.

He landed here in 1884 and shortly thereafter got a job in Thomas Edison's laboratory in New Jersey. But this did not last long. The young engineer was bursting with new ideas of his own and needed other surroundings to carry them out. As a result, in 1887, he formed an electrical research company and promptly began to put many of his pet theories to work.

In rapid succession Tesla brought into existence a series of electrical inventions that gave him a solid and renowned standing in that field. He developed more efficient motors for producing alternating current, which increased the usefulness of electricity, designed and built the Tesla transformer, and in 1893 he proposed a method for transmitting messages without wires. He had a whole host of electrical firsts with new and improved dynamos, transformers, coils and many other devices. But it was his ability to foresee the possible uses of electrical energy that caused the lifting of eyebrows in scientific circles and gave him a reputation as a visionary. Not the least startling of these ideas appeared in his remarks in a magazine article written in 1900 predicting the coming of radar.

In this article Tesla said, "When we raise the voice and hear an echo in reply, we know that the sound of the voice must have reached a distant wall or boundary, and must have been reflected from the same. Exactly as the sound, so an electrical wave is reflected, and the same evidence which is afforded by an echo is offered by an electrical phenomenon known as a 'stationary' wave. Instead of sending sound-vibrations toward a distant wall, I have sent electrical-vibrations towards the remote boundaries of the earth, and instead of the wall the earth has replied." From this Tesla went on to make his significant prediction. "By their use (Stationary Waves) we may produce at will, from a sending station, an electrical effect in any particular region of the globe; we may determine the relative position or course of a moving object, such as a vessel at sea, the distance traversed by the same, or its speed." With these words Nikola Tesla had anticipated radar by almost forty years.

More than twenty years later Tesla's ideas on a possible radar device were substantiated by a scientist of even greater renown, Guglielmo Marconi. After his invention of the wireless telegraph in 1896, Marconi devoted himself to research in the little known field of ultra-short electric waves. As a result of these labors, he foresaw even more vividly than Tesla the possibility of radar and particularly its value to mankind. In 1922, in an address before a gathering of radio and electrical engineers, he revealed his ideas on this still unborn electronic apparatus.

"As was first shown by Hertz, electric waves can be completely reflected by conducting bodies. In some of my tests I have noticed the effects of reflection and deflection of these waves by metallic objects miles away. It seems to me that it should be possible to design apparatus by means of which a ship could radiate or project a divergent beam of these rays in any desired direction, which rays, if coming across a metallic object, such as another steamer or ship, would be reflected back to a receiver

34

screen from the local transmitter on the sending ship, and thereby immediately reveal the presence and bearing of the other ship in fog or thick weather.

"One further great advantage of such an arrangement would be that it would be able to give warning of the presence and bearing of ships, even should these ships be unprovided with any kind of radio."*

Marconi went on to urge his listeners to spend more time studying the shorter electrical waves with the prospect of reaping even greater rewards than those obtained at the time with the longer variety. Apparently his words were taken seriously by his audience as well as the electrical profession in general. Soon the first experimental radar sets began to appear. Truly a creature of international origin, radar was born almost at the same time in the United States, England, France, and Germany.

Although Marconi had urged in his speech in 1922 that increased attention should be given to the mysterious behavior of ultra-short electric waves, there were scientists, both in Europe and America, already busily engaged in just such studies. One of the real pioneers in this work in the United States was Dr. Albert Hoyt Taylor, a physicist and electrical scientist connected with the Naval Research Laboratory. During the very same year that Marconi was predicting the possibilities of radar, Dr. Taylor and his associates were observing the unusual behavior of these radio waves in a number of interesting experiments.

In the fall of 1922, while working with an associate, Leo C. Young, Dr. Taylor was impressed with the action of a particular type of radio wave which, when aimed at steel buildings and ships, had a strong reflecting quality. This interest was increased enormously a short while later when Taylor and his colleagues made further tests along this line. They set up a radio transmitter on one side of the Potomac River and a receiver on the other. The research workers noticed that every time a boat

---

* Proceedings of the I.R.E.

passed up or down the river, it interrupted the path of the radio signals which were being sent out on certain frequencies. Every time this occurred, the receiver would become disturbed with a distinct interference pattern.

During the years 1925-1930, this reflecting ability of radio waves and a newly developed technique of transmitting these in pulse form were used in studies of the earth's atmosphere layers. Gregory Breit and Merle A. Tuve, scientists associated with the Carnegie Institution, pioneered the use of this radio tool for measuring the height of the ionosphere. The ionosphere is a gaseous, ionized shield forming one of the topmost levels in our atmosphere blanket. Because of its electrified nature, it causes radio signals to rebound back to earth, thus making possible our system of wireless and radio communication. These experiments confirmed the work of two other physicists, Kennelly and Heaviside, who first proposed the theoretical nature of the ionosphere.

All this experimental work strengthened the faint beginnings of an idea in the minds of scientists to employ electromagnetic waves for more practical purposes. In November, 1930, for example, Dr. Taylor noted in a report to his superiors in the Navy Department the significance of radio waves bouncing back from objects in motion. The Navy was impressed with the scientist's observations. Accordingly, in January, 1931, a project was established in the Radio Division of the Bureau of Engineering for developing a device which, in the words of the official assignment, was to "investigate use of radio to detect the presence of enemy vessels and aircraft." From that moment radar as we know it today in this country had its beginning.

Although the method for transmitting waves for detection purposes was quickly established and put in workable form, progress during the Thirties at first was rather slow. The pulse technique, rather than a continuous flow of waves, was preferred even at this early date by electronic scientists and engineers. Many difficult technical problems had to be solved. In 1932, in a report to his superiors, Dr. Taylor revealed a few of the obstacles that slowed the efforts of himself and his associates. For example, there was a need for some sort of automatic device that could collect, record and make use of the data resulting from the radio echo. In the case of oncoming enemy aircraft the unit would have to be able to tell their position and speed. As though in answer to Dr. Taylor's request, two scientists working in the Naval Research Laboratory shortly thereafter created just such a computer device, for that in essence is what it was. Although crude in form, the computer nevertheless hastened the day when the first experimental radar sets could be brought out of the laboratory and tested in the field.

Radar development received a strong impetus along about the mid-Thirties when the Army's Signal Corps laboratory entered the picture. The Navy had previously let its sister-service in on the secret nature of Dr. Taylor's experimental work and Army officers were deeply impressed with what they saw. They quickly realized that such radio-detecting apparatus would be particularly valuable if used with anti-aircraft guns to ward off hostile planes. Officials of the War Department shortly thereafter initiated similar experimental projects. With radar research teams now greatly expanded, these efforts began to bear fruit with a good deal more speed.

On December 14, 1936, the Signal Corps completed work on one of the first radar sets to be tested outside of a laboratory. It was a portable unit having a very limited detecting range, but it did succeed in spotting an airplane in flight. In that same year the Navy placed some experimental radar apparatus aboard its ships and tests proved highly promising. The following year they equipped the destroyer U.S.S. *Leary* with a complete but rather crude type of radar. The apparatus performed with considerable success, and those involved with its development were greatly encouraged. Signal Corps radar experimenters, meanwhile, determined not to be outdone by others, showed off a radar unit in February, 1937, that could spot airplanes twenty-

Early type United States Signal Corps radar apparatus. *U. S. Army Signal Corps.*

three miles away. This set was further refined until by November, 1938, it was performing with such effectiveness that the Army ordered it placed in production. The Signal Corps' radar unit contained position-finding equipment and was intended for defense use operating closely with anti-aircraft guns and searchlights. Radar was rapidly emerging from the laboratory as the Thirties drew to a close.

Following the promising trials of radar aboard the U.S.S. *Leary*, the Navy placed greatly improved equipment on the battleship U.S.S. *New York*. During maneuvers the radar set was subjected to particularly severe tests, but it came through with flying colors. Indeed, so well did it perform that a Naval officer remarked, "Radar is one of the most important radio developments since the advent of radio itself." This observation was to be confirmed many times over in the years ahead, particularly during the crisis-packed period of World War II.

During the early years of that world conflict, radar developments entered another phase. With a never-ending need for new defense weapons to counteract the blows of the enemy, military officials in this country realized that radar research would have to be expanded enormously if its full potential as a valuable defense weapon was to be realized. Thus, along with a great increase in the number of their own laboratory research workers, they also enlisted the help of industrial and university research centers. One of the most important of these groups was the Radiation Laboratory. This was established for the express purpose of exploring thoroughly all possible ways to improve the effectiveness of radar and thereby widen its military usefulness.

The Radiation Laboratory was set up at the Massachusetts Institute of Technology in November, 1940, and drew upon the talents of scientists and engineers from all sections of the country. At the height of its activity, close to 4,000 people were intensely engaged there in investigating improved methods for producing and detecting electromagnetic waves. In a little more than five years of existence, the organization could claim credit for an impressive series of radar accomplishments.

In any discussion of radar developments in this country during World War II, one cannot overlook the valuable assistance contributed by British scientists. Of course, as the war progressed, this became a two-way process, since as allies the two countries maintained a constant exchange of technical ideas. The result was a swift and continuing advance in the performance of radar. Great Britain had begun independent research in radar about the middle of the Thirties. By the end of that decade her scientists had developed radio-detecting apparatus that worked extremely well. Indeed, military authorities were so impressed with it that they had a chain of radar defense points erected along the eastern and southern British coasts. As matters turned out, this was none too soon. During the early months of World War II, Hitler's Luftwaffe tried to knock England out with

A typical magnetron tube of the kind used for producing microwaves. *Sylvania Electric Products, Inc.*

pulverizing air attacks. As one element in England's air defense, radar proved its value time and again. It helped spot the enemy planes long before they crossed the English Channel, enabling the R.A.F. to concentrate its outnumbered fighters where they could do the most damage to their opponents. If ever radar needed a test of its real worth and effectiveness, the air battles over Great Britain certainly provided this test. Some military authorities go so far as to say that radar's availability when the war began actually meant that country's survival.

One of the most important developments which British scientists brought to the attention of those in America was the invention of the magnetron. This was a new type of electron tube that created electrical impulses—called microwaves—which were even shorter than those used with the early radar sets. The magnetron brought about such an improvement in the performance of radar that modern detecting units are said to have had their beginning in its creation.

Before leaving this phase of the radar story, we should mention one other item. Although figures are often colorless and without meaning, in this instance they probably tell better than words the climax of radar's advancement during World

War II. In the period immediately preceding 1940 in the United States, radar as an industrial product was practically non-existent. At best, as our entrance into the world conflict came rapidly closer, radar was just beginning to go into production on a very limited scale. However, by the summer of 1945, as the war entered its final stages, the defense forces had acquired radar equipment worth almost three billion dollars. In addition, further orders totaling more than a billion and a half dollars were assigned for future delivery. Radar, first weakly nurtured by Heinrich Hertz in his laboratory in 1887, had grown to a stature far beyond the dreams of the most enthusiastic visionaries. Some observers who have closely watched the progress of radar feel that at no time in the history of the world has a scientific or industrial development expanded in so many different directions and on such a scale as has this radio-detecting equipment.

Radar Operation

The word "radar" was first introduced in 1941 to describe the newly developed electronic detecting equipment. A United States Naval officer was its originator, and its stands for "RA-dio D-etection A-nd R-anging." It is interesting to note that the word spells the same backward and forward, which in a way symbolizes the basic operation of the device.

Essentially radar is an electronic apparatus to detect through atmospheric barriers or at great distances the presence of unseen objects. It can also tell those using it how far away the object is, its position in relation to the ground observer and, if it is a moving target, its speed. Radar can determine the speed, whether the target is moving toward or away from the observer. All this is not magic but the action of flashing radio waves of ultra-short length in the form of "pulses" through the air by a powerful transmitter. These waves travel through space in a beam, like the rays of a searchlight. When this radar beam strikes an object, a radio signal is reflected back to the point where it originated. Bats utilize the same principle, sending out high-frequency sound waves to locate obstacles in the darkest caves and avoid hitting them.

A receiver—a cathode-ray-tube indicator usually located with the transmitter—picks up the returning radio echo and converts it into terms of distance from the object, a mathematics ratio based on the speed of electromagnetic waves as they move through space and the time involved in their transmission and reflection. In radar, the velocity of electromagnetic waves, 186,000 miles per second, is converted into a more manageable unit of measurement. The radar figure is based on the fact that a radio wave can travel one mile out and one mile back, a distance known as a radar mile, in 10.75 microseconds. A microsecond is a time unit equivalent to one-millionth of a second. A radio wave can cover about one-fifth of a mile in a single microsecond, a time lapse often designated as μ sec, the symbol being the Greek letter "mu."

When a radar pulse is flashed to a target, it really makes the journey twice—going out as a signal and coming back as an echo. However, the round-trip time needed for a radar pulse to strike a target and bounce back is the important factor with this "seeing" apparatus. The time element plus the speed with which a pulse travels determine the distance of the target from the radio transmitter. This may be compared to the principle of the echo as demonstrated by sound waves which travel 1,100 feet a second. If you were to shout toward a nearby cliff or other object and the echo returned in two seconds, you would know that the object was 1,100 feet distant.

Basically radar operates the same way except, of course, electromagnetic waves move at an incredibly faster rate. Because of this last fact, no mechanical device is capable of handling the distance-measuring ability of radar. This job must be done by electronics, the most important element of which is the cathode-ray tube.

The electronic equipment used today for transmitting re-

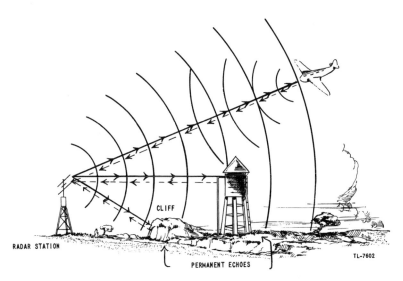

Diagram shows operation of radar.

flecting radio waves to obtain this information is a far cry from the simple, crude apparatus used by Hertz. Radar is an extremely complex affair. But despite the fact that it has been developed into a variety of forms for many special jobs, this extraordinary equipment has basic parts common to all. To understand better the operation of radar, we must know something of its more important individual parts.

The power supply can probably be called the basic element in radar because it provides the electrical energy needed for all the units to function. In some cases, mainly military, this power is produced by a mobile generator. Normally, however. the power supply is obtained from available electric power lines. One of the more important units which it puts into action is known as the modulator.

The modulator, in a way, is the traffic cop of radar. It controls the on-and-off operation of the transmitter with a timing sequence of microsecond precision. This is a vital part in the exacting task of producing and transmitting the stream of

43

powerful pulses necessary for locating objects. It provides the transmitter with a high voltage of direct current in the form of extremely brief pulses, about one-millionth of a second and less. After each pulse the transmitter is silent while the receiving unit waits for the returning echo. This pattern is repeated more than 1,000 times a second and has a close relationship to the minimum distance over which targets can be detected.

The great bursts of electrical energy which radar sends through the air in the form of electromagnetic pulses originate in and are sent out by the transmitter. The heart of this radar component is the magnetron, the electronic tube which produces the powerful reflecting radio pulses. English scientists created the magnetron during the early years of World War II. They were quick to recognize that the type of radio waves which it created, far shorter in length and more powerful than those originated by other electron tubes then in use, made for a vastly more sensitive radar apparatus. It has been said that the magnetron, subsequently brought to this country and improved by scientists at the Radiation Laboratory, marked the turning point in the development of radar. From a somewhat crude, unreliable device it was changed almost overnight into the precision instrument that it is today.

Since the day when the magnetron was first introduced into the field of radar, many different types have been developed. Basically cylindrical diodes, they all operate pretty much the same way to produce their enormous amounts of pulsed electrical energy. Clouds of electrons swirl about the cathode, in the center of the tube, in complicated patterns. They are set in motion and controlled by a combination of electrical and magnetic forces. Magnetrons have many ways for storing their high-frequency radio energy, the most common of which are cavities that circle the outer perimeter of the tube. This energy is in the form of split-second powerful pulses which are usually carried away from the magnetron by a wave guide. The latter, a hollow tube-like device, is hooked up to the magnetron. The high-frequency radio pulses flow through the tube—like water through a pipe—to the antenna, and are beamed into the air.

If we had to name the single item connected with radar that would symbolize this radio-detecting equipment, we would perhaps choose the antenna reflector. The reflector has one other characteristic, namely that it is probably made into more different sizes and shapes than any other component of radar. The reason for this is that each radar antenna reflector is designed to perform a particular job. Some are made to flash a narrow beam of microwaves, others, a wide beam. This may be

Antenna for Raytheon's new Mariners' Pathfinder Radar. *Raytheon Manufacturing Co.*

Another of the many radar antenna types is the small dish-shape model. This is commonly used with automatic and rapid-firing anti-aircraft guns. *Official U. S. Navy Photograph.*

done in a fanwise vertical direction or horizontally. Then there are radar reflectors that keep rotating 360°, made especially for scanning the skies for airplanes. These can be altered so that they move within a restricted arc, covering only a portion of the sky. Some can also be made to rotate faster than others.

All types of radar antenna reflectors can either send out microwaves or receive them. To help them do this, they receive a helping hand from wave guides, which as we have already seen, are shaped somewhat like tubes with rectangular interiors. Wave guides also form an actual part of antennas which may consist of short metal rods called dipoles fixed at right angles to

This is a "venetian blind" type of radar search antenna. The bent tube at the left is the wave guide. The antenna is located atop an 80-foot tower at the Los Angeles International Airport and is capable of rotating 360 degrees. The information which it picks up is sent by coaxial cable to the CAA Control Tower where observers can advise pilots of approaching aircraft of their exact positions and help them to land safely. The radar antenna can survey an area of 2,800 square miles. *Gilfillan Bros., Inc.*

The radar antenna in the foreground is known as the "orange peel" or "beaver tail" type. Its specialty is to seek out and determine the altitude of airplanes. The antenna moves with a dipping action. The large antenna in the background is able to determine the altitude, distance, direction and speed of aircraft up to 200 miles from the set. The top portion revolves at about 10 revolutions per minute. *Air Force Photo.*

their sides. The antenna can also be shaped like a horn fitted to the open end of the wave guide. It is usually located at the bottom of the reflector, at what is called the focal point. The wave guides act as a super-highway for the pulses generated by the magnetron. These pulses or microwaves streak along the hollow wave guides and are sprayed out against the reflector by the antenna. From here the microwaves flash outward through the air. Antenna-reflectors cannot receive echoes while sending out microwaves.

When the fast-moving microwaves have struck their target and are reflected back to the radar apparatus, the reflector picks up the fainter radio echo and transfers it to the antenna, which

47

funnels it back through the wave guide. But now, thanks to another electronic device which we shall see shortly, the radio signal is directed to the receiver rather than the magnetron, where it is amplified to much greater power and then flashed on the face of the radar indicator—the cathode-ray tube.

The cathode-ray tube is an electronic device that shows visually the transmission and reception of radar signals. More important, it is the key for converting time intervals into equivalent terms for measuring distance. As with antennas, there are a number of different indicator types, each designed to do a specific task. Two of the more common are called the A-scope and the PPI-scope, or Plan Position Indicator scope. The A-scope is the simpler, indicating only the range to a target. The PPI-scope, on the other hand, not only gives the range but also

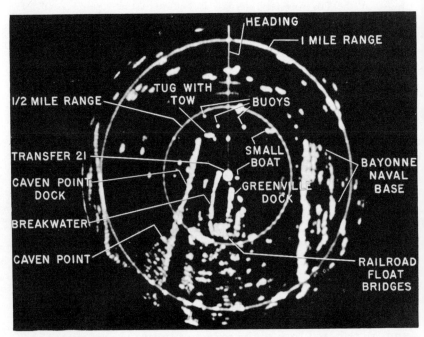

A typical radar view as seen on a PPI-scope. This scene shows a portion of the New Jersey side of New York Harbor. *Sperry Gyroscope Company, Inc.*

48

the direction of the target from the radar apparatus. To understand better what these radar indicators are like, picture a television tube, which they closely resemble in appearance and operation.

Basically all radar-indicating cathode-ray tubes are composed of an electron gun which converts transmitted and echo-radar signals into an electron beam and coils which deflect this beam. There is a fluorescent coating on the back of the tube's face, which changes the electron energy into visible light. With the A-scope, the radar signals are changed into a thin, accurate beam of electrons. The end of this beam strikes the fluorescent screen and is converted into a bright spot of light called a "pip," electronic language for target. British radar operators call this spot of light a "blip."

The electron beam moves across the face of the scope radially to the outer edge and at an even rate of speed. It begins this movement at the very instant that a radar pulse is flashed outward. The distance which the beam has traveled to the right from its starting point is in direct proportion to the distance the pulse has covered since leaving the antenna. As the electron beam travels swiftly to the edge of the scope, it traces a faint, even line of light which radar operators call a "sweep."

The electron beam undergoes a distinct change when the echo signal arrives. The returning radio pulse carrying target information causes an increase in the number and speed of electrons in the beam striking the scope face. This produces a brilliant spot of light or "pip" on the indicator. The "pip" forms at the place where the electron beam happens to be hitting at the precise moment the echo signal is arriving.

The distance of the "pip" from the point where the sweep began is a measure of the distance the radio pulse covered in flashing to the target and back. Even though the sweep line goes on to the edge of the scope and then shoots back to the center, the "pip" will continue to glow after it passes. The face of the scope is usually marked off with concentric rings

A giant transparent plastic board used by radar observers to plot the positions of targets picked up on the scope. *U. S. Army Photograph.*

representing a scale of miles. Thus, wherever a "pip" happens to fall within these rings, an observer can tell instantly the range of the target from the detecting equipment.

The PPI-scope not only reveals the range of a target as we have already pointed out, but also its direction. In this tube the electron beam of radar signals is aimed directly at the center of the scope. This beam, transformed into a solid sweep line on the face of the indicator, also travels from the center of the scope to the outer edge. However, it rotates about its center, a movement synchronized with the rotation of the antenna.

When the antenna faces a particular point of the compass, so too will the sweep line. If the radar beam strikes objects

50

north, east, south and west as the antenna whirls 360°, echoes will appear as "pips" on the scope, "painting" a continuous picture of the area being scanned. The direction of each of the "pips" indicated from the center of the scope is the true direction of the objects from the radar equipment. The radar apparatus always represents the center of the PPI-scope. The distance of the "pips" from the center of the tube's face indicates the distance separating the target and radar. The PPI-scope presents a polar-map-like presentation of the region being surveyed.

The face of the PPI-scope is also marked off into an accurate scale, usually concentric circles, so that the radar data is readily available. Normally the cathode-ray tube works in close harmony with the receiver. This part of radar equipment picks up the returning weak radar echo and amplifies it to greater strength before passing it on to the tube.

Finally there are two other units that play important roles in radar operation, especially if a single antenna is used both for sending and receiving. These are known as the T-R Box and the A-T-R Box. One stands for transmit-receive and the other for anti-transmit-receive. Both of these electronic devices act like switches on a railroad. They prevent fast-moving radio signals from traveling along the wrong track.

When the magnetron is ready to flash its powerful frequency to the antenna, the A-T-R Box opens the switch to let it pass through, while the T-R Box blocks off the receiver portion of radar to prevent it from being burned out by the enormous burst of electrical energy.

At the very instant that the radar echo returns, the T-R Box opens the switch and guides it to the receiver, while the A-T-R Box cuts off the track that would lead to the transmitter. In this way the weak returning signal is prevented from losing still more of its strength before reaching the radar indicator screen. Both these electronic units operate by means of gas-filled tubes. While they are ionized or electrified, the pulse passes through the A-T-R Box as the T-R Box closes off the receiver. Between pulse transmissions, the tube become de-ionized and just the reverse of the above action takes place with the echo serving as the signal.

Ionization, involving the electrification of gases, is an interesting electronic action. Gases are made up of atoms and molecules electrically neutral in nature. However, when some force such as an electric current is introduced into the gas, the electron make-up of the molecules or atoms is disturbed. One or more electrons dislodge themselves from the molecules, leaving the latter positively charged. The free electrons may also attach themselves to other molecules, making them electrically negative in nature. Molecules changed in this way are called

This is a typical radar console used for precision approach in the GCA blind landing system. *I. T. & T.*

ions, and the process is called ionization. The particles of gas that have now become electrified are capable of conducting an electric current. When the external force is cut off, the ions revert back to their original molecular state and the gas ceases to be an electrical conductor.

Now that we have reviewed some of the more important units of which radar is composed, let us see briefly how they work as a whole. First the power supply activates the modulator, which in turn triggers the transmitter that produces the radar pulse. This is flashed along to the antenna, which beams it through the air. When an echo is received, the antenna catches it and guides it along to the receiver. The receiver increases the strength of the echo and then passes it along to the cathode-ray tubes, where it is converted into a "pip." Thus, through the magic of electronics man has increased his own vision a hundredfold, regardless of weather, distance or nightfall on land, sea and in the air.

World War II Radar

Before we had radar at our disposal, soldiers operating anti-aircraft guns had to pick up the sound of oncoming enemy planes by means of huge horns called locators. With the help of telescopes and other optical equipment the soldiers would get their sights on the target and attempt to shoot it down. For night operation, they had to spot the airplanes with searchlighs before they could aim their guns. The horn apparatus had its origin in the World War I and until airplanes achieved their present speeds, the sound system was fairly effective. But airplane velocities did not remain static, and by the time World War II began, the sound system used to detect their approach had become obsolete. One of the prime reasons radar was developed, in fact, was to provide military forces with a more effective way for spotting hostile airplanes.

Once military leaders were convinced that radar was indeed the answer to their problem, they swamped scientists and engineers with orders for all sorts of radar equipment for fighting purposes. Land, sea and air forces all clamored for radar sets to suit their specialized military needs. Before the war came to an end, military groups had acquired not only a number of different kinds of radar units but also a whole assortment of the most astonishing electronic equipment the world had yet seen.

Because one of the earliest ideas associated with the use of radar was for airplane detection work, ground troops operating anti-aircraft guns were among the first to put it in operation. The country that pioneered this application for radar was Great Britain, which started to establish, as far back as 1935, a series of such "seeing" posts throughout southern and eastern England. By the time that country entered World War II, the number had greatly increased.

These early radar units, although not as accurate or efficient, perhaps, as the microwave models which were to appear in 1943 and 1944, proved far superior in performance to the old sound systems. The radar sets not only warned of airplanes approaching while they were still many miles away, but they could also locate their position in relation to the radar unit and reveal their altitude. It was largely because of radar that the heroic and far-outnumbered R.A.F. defenders could mass their planes far in advance and at just the right spot to meet the surprised German airmen. As German planes were shot down by dozens, the Luftwaffe was forced to abandon its daylight raids.

But even when the enemy air force attacked only at night, radar continued its excellent defensive work. Practical airborne radar units had not yet appeared, so these ground installations, which could see both the attacking and defending planes on the scope, had to guide the pilot of the defending plane to his target by means of radio communication. This extremely difficult maneuver was abandoned just as soon as airborne radar appeared. After that the ground radar operator guided the defending plane only until the target appeared on the pilot's own radar set.

By 1940 American ground and sea forces began receiving radar units in increasing numbers. Many early radar sets were rushed to the Canal Zone and Pearl Harbor, two of our more vital defense points in World War II. It is a matter of record that radar actually spotted the coming of Japanese planes while they were still about 135 miles away from Pearl Harbor on December 7, 1941. However, it was mistakenly thought that they were United States Air Force planes, and therefore no defensive measures were taken.

These pioneer Army radar sets, developed by the Signal Corps laboratories, were, like most others then in existence, a far cry from those which were later to use microwaves. The early models used radio waves measured in feet instead of inches, like the more advanced types. Antenna assemblies were of varied shapes and sizes, but most often of a large, rectangular shape frequently compared in appearance to a large bed spring. These antennas sent out a broad beam which did not permit the pinpoint accuracy of those used with microwaves. Then as now much of this Army radar equipment was highly mobile. Transmitters, receivers and generators were placed in giant trailers so they could be hauled quickly to any particular locality where it was felt enemy planes might attack.

The Army radar models of the early Forties were as effective as those used by the British in revealing the compass direction of an enemy plane as well as its height and distance. They helped anti-aircraft gunners improve their marksmanship whether planes were attacking at night or in overcast skies or fog. Good as this radar equipment was, it experienced a vast improvement through perfection of the technique for producing microwaves. One model used by ground defenders against attacking enemy planes was known as the SCR-584, which began to appear in 1943. It was considered the best detecting equipment of its kind used either by the Allies or the enemy.

The Army Signal Corps laboratories, together with those of certain industries, helped to bring into being radar apparatus which was capable not only of tracking a target automatically but also of aiming the guns. Once the antenna was pointed at a target, electronic devices actuated small motors called servo-mechanisms, which kept the antenna pointing steadily at its aerial object. The signals obtained by the antenna were fed to a computer, an "electronic brain," which directed other devices in such a way as to keep the guns aimed constantly at the mark. Anti-aircraft batteries using this automatic detecting and aiming equipment established amazing records of hits with a minimum of ammunition. The SCR-584 played a particularly valuable role in England in 1944 when the Germans began bombarding that country with Buzz-Bombs. The great majority of these pilotless aerial weapons were shot down with the help of this American-developed radar set with its "electronic brain."

The United States Navy, as we have already seen, was among the pioneers in developing radar for detection work. This was designed not only for spotting aircraft but surface ships as well. Much of this equipment was similar to that employed by the Army except that it was adapted to meet the special needs of shipboard use. Some of it weighed tons. By the time this country was in the thick of World War II, almost every major ship in the fleet had some form of radar aboard. This included the most advanced types such as the Army had for automatically tracking a target and controlling the aim of anti-aircraft guns.

Of equal importance with its service in air defense was radar's use by battleships and cruisers at night or in bad weather to blast with their guns enemy surface ships. Radar "pips," by showing where the shells splashed in the water on misses, made it easy to correct the gunner's aim. In some of the heaviest naval battles against the Japanese fleet, enemy ships were sunk in this manner. A particular instance occurred one night in the South Pacific when a United States battleship picked up a Japanese ship on its radar scope. Bombardment began shortly thereafter and soon the enemy ship was afire and sinking, although a distance of eight miles separated the two vessels.

Perhaps of all the varied radar equipment produced during World War II that used by military airplanes was the most interesting. This was not only because of the different purposes for which it was intended—searching out enemy surface ships, hostile aircraft, "seeing" targets through overcast skies and at night and for navigational use—but because some of the biggest technical puzzles had to be solved before radar could be made for airplanes. It was mainly through this activity that the magnetron was created and developed. Scientists and engineers had to find new kinds of electronic devices for producing powerful radio frequencies to replace the normally bulky parts of radar unsuited for use in the air. Smaller and less complicated equipment was needed for limited aircraft space. The magnetron helped because, for one thing, the microwaves which it developed could be radiated and picked up by a far smaller antenna system than that required on sets using longer waves.

One of the research groups that accomplished a great deal toward this goal was the Radiation Laboratory in the United States. In a little more than six months after scientists at this research center became familiar with the magnetron, they had developed a compact and very effective radar unit for use aboard fighter planes. This detecting equipment could spot an enemy plane several miles away.

A technique worked out for night fighter air tactics by Allied strategists called for close cooperation between a ground radar operator and the pilot of the plane. The ground controller would be able to watch both the attacking and defense planes on his scope. He would issue instructions to the defense pilot guiding his plane toward that of the enemy. When the ground-based radar operator felt that the defending airman was close enough, he instructed the pilot to turn on his own radar. The enemy target would then appear on the airborne scope and the battle would begin. This radar guidance technique, although greatly improved, is still employed for defense against possible sky raiders.

One of the most important military uses of airborne radar was in search operations aboard patrol planes. Enemy submarines and surface ships were hunted down and often destroyed by radar-equipped patrol planes. This equipment, a variation of fighter plane radar, appeared in two forms. One, a neatly streamlined lightweight unit, hung outside the body of the plane like a bomb. The other was built in special compartments within the fuselage. The external radar attachment weighed less than 200 pounds. A newly developed saucer-like antenna assembly, fixed to the front end of the unit but hidden within the streamlined covering, radiated and caught the reflected signals.

Once the effectiveness of air-to-surface search radar became established and recognized, it proved one of the most valuable defense weapons in the fight against enemy submarines. It has been estimated that throughout much of 1943 when the U-boat menace was at its worst, these prowlers of the ocean depths were being sent to the bottom at a rate of almost one a day. Allied aircraft equipped with radar are said to have accounted for more than fifty per cent of these victims. Surface enemy ships were also likely targets for radar-carrying Allied patrol planes.

In the Pacific theater of war a single squadron of patrol bombers connected with the United States 14th Air Force sent 110,000 tons of Japanese cargo ships to the bottom of the China Sea in a single month. What made this accomplishment outstanding was the fact that the planes went out only at night, using radar to spot their targets.

The air arm of the United States Navy made particularly extensive use of patrol planes because they could search far greater areas of the ocean than surface vessels. Indeed, their daily operations became so important that the planes first assigned, crudely adapted from other models, gave way to newer aircraft specially designed for the purpose. One of the first in this new family of patrol bombers was the four-engine Privateer. With a cruising range of more than 2,000 miles, this plane had an exceptionally long nose which was crammed with the latest in radar, long-range radio equipment, radar direction-finder and other electronic devices. Large plastic domes, or "blisters," were spotted in a number of places throughout the fuselage. These covered antennas. The "blisters" gave the plane an odd appearance and because of these, servicemen were quick to nickname it the "Wart-hog."

As scientists and engineers found newer ways to make airborne radar more compact and effective, novel ideas for using the equipment kept pace with the technical developments. Since airplane radar could tell a pilot if there were objects in front of him or on either side, it occurred to somebody that the unit might also serve to warn of oncoming planes at the rear. As a result, a special radar device was produced for installation in the tail of a plane. A special light on the instrument panel would blink whenever the tail radar detected a would-be attacker. Sometimes a bell was substituted to alert the flyer.

With the development of radar devices for searching out other hostile aircraft and enemy surface ships, there followed inevitably the introduction of airborne radar equipment to help in bombing operations. A special impetus in this direction was the introduction of the shorter radar microwaves combined with the PPI-scope. Since radar pulses reflect better from land than from sea, microwaves and the PPI-scope provided an almost map-like presentation of the territory within the observation range of the plane. Coastlines, rivers, harbors, bridges, and many other features of a sprawling land target were clearly shown on the bombardier's radar screen regardless of the weather.

Bombing missions carried out with the help of radar were called BTO or "bombing through overcast." Once the technique of using this equipment was mastered, bombing-runs over German targets were accomplished on a regular schedule. Previously it had been mostly a hit or miss affair, dependent to a large extent on favorable weather conditions. The first units for the United States Air Force use were created by the Radiation Laboratory in the summer of 1943. By November 3 of that year, American flyers were ready to put the equipment through its first practical test. Nine planes attached to the bomber command of the 8th Air Force were outfitted with these radar bombsights. Each of these craft, nicknamed "Pathfinders" by the British R.A.F., led a group of 60 planes to their German target.

Wilhelmshaven, the objective for this particular test raid, had on former missions often been missed by bombers using only visual sights. As the planes neared their target, the city was completely hidden beneath a thick blanket of clouds. But the radar-equipped Pathfinder pilots clearly saw the sprawling town on their scopes and unerringly led the air fleet to its mark. The Pathfinders dropped brilliant flares which lighted the ground target, and using these as a guide, the swarm of bombers dropped their destructive cargoes. Reconnaissance photos taken at a later date showed that the bombs struck their marks unerringly, thanks to radar's all-seeing eye. Following this initial success, radar-equipped Pathfinder planes played an important role in almost every succeeding bombing-run over Germany.

Additional radar equipment for military planes was also developed with an entirely different function. This radar apparatus was concerned largely with the navigational problems of an aircraft's flight. Several systems were originated around this radar equipment, the "Oboe" and the "H" by the British, and the "Shoran," which was produced by American electronic scientists. "Shoran" stands for "short range navigation."

The Oboe arrangement called for installation of an airborne radar beacon in a plane. A beacon is a radar pulse transmitter that sends out strong repeated signals. Two ground-based radar stations flash pulses to the beacon which responds with signals of its own. The beacon's signals are much more powerful than conventional radar echoes, and in some cases this is considered an important advantage. After the beacon's pulses are recorded at the ground stations, the airplane's position is precisely located by means of triangulation. Knowing the exact distance of a specific target from the two radar land bases, observers at one of these radar bases are able to signal a bomber crew when they have reached their bomb-release point.

Great accuracy was claimed for Oboe. Aircraft bomber crews could drop their destructive cargoes with an error of less than 800 feet from altitudes of about 6 miles. This radar navigation-bombing system had a range of slightly less than 300 miles. The German industrial Ruhr was one of the favorite targets of Allied bombing planes using Oboe for guidance.

The H and Shoran systems were pretty much the same in that they required a pair of radar beacons to be located at exact points on the ground. Aircraft carried the radar equipment that activated the beacons and recorded their responses. An operator aboard a bombing plane, for example, would flash a radar pulse first to one station and then to the other on an alternate basis. The beacons would reply with signals of their own. A radar scope aboard the plane indicated the pulses when received and, with other intricate electronic devices, helped to convert them into terms of distance between the aircraft and ground stations.

These two radar navigation systems had about the same effective range as Oboe. Shoran is still being employed to good advantage by both military and commercial aircraft. It has also been adapted for use by ships at sea.

Radar beacons were adapted by Allied air forces for another purpose, to distinguish friendly planes from those of the enemy. This arrangement was known as Identification Friend or Foe (IFF for short). Allied planes would carry an airborne beacon that responded with a coded signal when interrogated by a ground-based radar unit. Planes not answering with the proper code signal were looked upon with suspicion. IFF was not too successful, especially after air fleets began to grow to huge numbers with the progress of the war.

When British and American bomber fleets began their systematic destruction of Germany, its fighter planes threw up a stubborn defense. Their toll of Allied bombers was extremely high on many air raids. Because of this tough opposition, Allied scientists and engineers had to produce weapons with radar attachments so that bomber crews could protect themselves more effectively. One of these devices, a radar range finder, quickly and accurately gave the distance between the bomber and an attacking fighter plane, enabling Allied airmen to aim and fire their guns with far deadlier effect.

A variation of this radar range-finder, which not only detected enemy planes but also helped to aim the guns, was developed for night fighting. This radar gunnery equipment was extremely advanced for its time, but since it appeared very late in the war, got little use. The postwar years, however, have witnessed its continued development and today military planes are equipped with amazing radar-electronic armament devices that automatically spot, aim, and fire the guns.

The radar developments for military aircraft discussed so far were certainly important from the point of view of advancing the destructiveness of air warfare. In many respects, however, these were overshadowed by still another World War II radar development that helped airmen bring their planes down during times of poor visibility. This was called the Ground Control Approach system, or GCA for short. It was significant not only because it helped Allied flyers returning from bombing or fighter missions to complete their trip safely when the home base was hidden by a blanket of fog, but because it went on to still greater success during the postwar years, adding to the safety record of commercial air transportation.

GCA consists of ground-based radar units located at or near the runway of an airfield. Two types of radar sets are used. One is for search purposes and picks up a particular plane destined to land while it is still some distance from the airfield, usually within a range of 30 miles. This is known as surveillance radar.

The radar antenna and trailer vans housing electronic equipment are a part of the Ground Control Approach system for landing airplanes in bad weather. This mobile unit is attached to the United States Air Force. *Air Force Photo.*

When the operator of the long-range radar picks up the correct plane, he guides the pilot by means of radio communication to make the proper maneuvers for lining up his plane with the runway. As the incoming plane approaches to within less than ten miles of the edge of this runway, the second and more precise operating radar unit takes over. It is called the precision approach radar equipment. Its accuracy is such that it permits the detection of a plane's variation of 10 feet in elevation at 1 mile and 20 feet in azimuth, or side to side direction.

By watching the PPI-scope the operator can tell with great exactness whether the pilot is bringing the plane in too high, too low, or wide of the runway. Radio communications enable the ground controller to tell the pilot at all times what his relation is to the runway until the plane's wheels touch down. Very often it is not necessary to talk to the pilot all the way down until contact with the runway has been made. The pilot frequently breaks through the poor visibility barrier near ground level so that he can bring in his plane for the final landing maneuver without further assistance. With this radar blind landing system, no equipment is needed aboard the plane except the usual radio set.

For military purposes, GCA equipment was housed in trailers so that it could be moved to any particular runway desired. Even today, much of this radar apparatus is in mobile form for the same reason. At civilian airfields which use it, however, GCA is usually a permanent installation. For the best example of how radar has advanced from the days of World War II, we need only consider GCA equipment then and now. At that time sixteen men were required to operate radar blind landing apparatus. Today a single man can do the same chore.

Not all of the amazing radar weapons produced during World War II were meant for warning or detecting purposes. There was a group of devices that made use of reflected radio waves for an entirely different task—destruction. One such was the radar proximity fuse. This deadly weapon—which was literally radar in explosive action—was among the best kept secrets of the war. It turned out to be a most unpleasant surprise to the enemy.

The proximity fuse was part of an anti-aircraft or artillery shell that did not require contact with a target to explode. It consisted of a tiny radio transmitter-receiver which sent out a

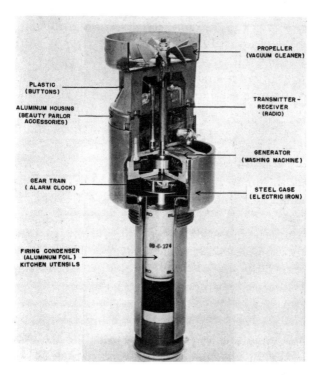

PROPELLER
(VACUUM CLEANER)

PLASTIC
(BUTTONS)

ALUMINUM HOUSING
(BEAUTY PARLOR
ACCESSORIES)

TRANSMITTER -
RECEIVER
(RADIO)

GENERATOR
(WASHING MACHINE)

GEAR TRAIN
(ALARM CLOCK)

STEEL CASE
(ELECTRIC IRON)

FIRING CONDENSER
(ALUMINUM FOIL)
KITCHEN UTENSILS

Cut-away view showing construction of proximity fuse developed by the National Bureau of Standards for the U. S. Army during World War II. Fuse screws into nose of bomb and explodes when its radio waves contact target. Words in parenthesis indicate some of the products lacking in wartime because of material shortage due to construction needs of fuse and other military items. *U. S. Army Photograph.*

continuous stream of radio waves while the shell was in flight. As the missile approached a target, usually at a distance of less than 100 feet, the waves would hit the object and be reflected back to the transmitter. These echoes, similar to those of "seeing" radar, would be picked up by the fuse's receiver, amplified and rushed through a miniature circuit to an electron tube called a thyratron. This tube acted as a switch which set off the explosive charge of the shell.

The fuse was cylindrical in shape, about 8″ long and 2½″ in

diameter. It was a marvel of technical accomplishment with its tiny, rugged electron tubes and compact circuit. Anti-aircraft shells equipped with proximity fuses did not have to make a direct hit in order to knock a plane out of the sky. The deadly shower of fragments which it unleashed near attacking aircraft proved sufficient to do the job. Radar proximity fuses were particularly helpful in warding off the hail of Buzz-Bombs aimed at England. These sensitive fuses were also attached to shells intended for land targets.

One of the most frequently heard phrases concerning the development of military weapons says in effect that for every new weapon produced, in due time there will appear an effective counterweapon. Throughout the history of war-making implements this belief has held true. Radar, which almost single handedly revolutionized warring tactics in World War II with its ability to "see" the enemy at night or through smoke and fog, was no exception.

The Japanese and Germans also had radar equipment which did equally important work for them in helping to ward off air attacks. Knowing through their own experience how valuable radar apparatus could be, the Allies worked night and day to find ways of neutralizing the effectiveness of the enemies' installations. Two main radar countermeasures came out of this effort. One consisted of jamming the enemy's radar transmitter and the other showering pieces of tinfoil from attacking bomber planes. This caused confused echoes to appear on the defense radar scope. A third technique, also effective, employed a radio direction finder. Using this electronic instrument to spot and locate an enemy installation, planes or a ground raiding party then went out to destroy it. This technique was employed a number of times against the Japanese-held islands of the Pacific

To jam an enemy's radar installation, the target—airplane or ship—had to have some device that would send out a radio signal to smother the signals or echoes being sent back to the radar transmitter. The countermeasure device used by the Allies was a special type of radio transmitter that could be tuned to the same channel as that used by the enemy's radar to transmit pulses. British and American airmen called such radio sets "carpets."

Once the radio transmitter began operating on the proper frequency channel, a disturbance appeared on the radar scope that looked like fine blades of grass. Echoes from an airplane are similar in nature—that is, vertical marks—so when the interference was created on the scope, the true echoes became lost in the "grass."

The tinfoil countermeasure—which the British called "window," the Americans "chaff," and the Germans "Dueppel"—was the most commonly used in World War II. This method took advantage of a weakness of radar which cannot tell the nature of small targets. An airplane or ship to radar are both small objects which cannot be distinguished. With this knowledge, scientists found that a number of metallic strips whose size has a direct relation to the wave length of the transmitted radar pulse would return a strong echo to the scope. When the tinfoil strips were tied in bundles weighing about two ounces and thrown from a plane, they returned a radar echo signal similar to that given off by a bomber.

The technique employed by the Allied air forces with this countermeasure was to dump a mass of these metal foil bundles from attacking bombers as they closed in on a target. Trailing out behind and below the planes, the metal "chaff" created a hopelessly confused jumble of false echoes on the radar scope so that the real echoes were completely lost.

The third countermeasure mentioned, the radio direction-finder, was of an entirely different nature from the two just described. It usually involved locating the enemy's land-based radar installation and destroying it. However, it was also used for hunting down radar-carrying enemy search planes. This radar countermeasure was based on the fact that radar pulses are extremely powerful and can be picked up by a suitable radio receiver with a directional antenna some distance from the source. A ring-shaped directional antenna containing a sensitive coil is attached to a vertical shaft that can be rotated in a complete circle. But it detects signals from only one direction. The early countermeasure units picked up the radar pulse as a distinctive sound. Later a more automatic device was developed that displayed the signals on a radar-like scope.

In operation, the antenna on the new type of receiver rotates slowly, searching for a stream of radar pulses. These will be detected only if the antenna is pointing toward them. Once the radar pulses have been captured they are flashed to a scope attached to the receiver unit. Here the signals are converted into a beam of light radiating from the center of the scope to its outer edge, like the spoke of a wheel. This beam points to the direction from which the enemy radar is sending out signals. If the beam, or scope trace, as it is called, points upward vertically from the center of the screen, it means the radar signal is coming from straight ahead. If the beam is horizontal and points to the right, it indicates the signal is coming from the starboard side of the plane or ship on which the receiver is located.

During the Sicilian invasion this Allied radar countermeasure was employed to seek out and destroy the enemy's radar installations on that island. The direction-finder equipment used at that time, however, was crude and did not have a rotating directional antenna or scope to pick up and indicate the signals. The pilot had to fly his plane in the region of a suspected radar station and point his craft in whatever direction the radar signals appeared to be originating. The loudness of the incoming signals told him when he was heading in the right direction.

When the war ended, radar's development and advancement did not stop. Throughout the postwar era this extraordinary electronic equipment has progressed to new heights of uncanny accomplishment, particularly in the world of peacetime activity.

Chapter Three

RADAR TODAY

Military Radar

Present-day airpower is based largely on jet propulsion. This has brought about an enormous increase in the speed of aircraft, which ranges between 600 and 700 miles per hour, and is almost double that of fighting planes in World War II. Jet fighters are also beginning to appear with a velocity approaching 1,000 miles per hour. This tremendous jump in airplane speeds has created new problems for the pilot. Because of the swiftness with which his plane moves through the air, the point has almost been reached where it is humanly impossible for him to tend to tasks other than maneuvering his aircraft. To help relieve the pilot of a fighter plane of many of his extra duties, radar and electronics are being employed more and more. The automatic radar-electronic gunsight is one of the newest and most valuable of the modern devices.

The radar-electronic gunsight works with lightning swiftness. Its electronic brain tells the pilot when his guns are accurately pointed at the target as two combat planes roar along at break-neck speed. It calculates quickly and automatically the speed of the bullet, the effect which gravity has on it and the correct firing angle to the target. This last mentioned factor—perhaps the most important—involves the radar unit. Radar continuously measures the distance between the hunted and the hunter, and the data it obtains is fed instantly to the electronic computer or "brain," as it is more popularly known. It is also the radar set that lets the pilot know when he is within correct shooting range. All the airman needs to do is to watch a lighted circle on his windshield and a spot within it. When the two are accurately superimposed on the target the pilot presses the trigger on the guns.

With the aid of the electronic "brain" and "eye," the pilot

can devote most of his attention to flying his airplane. Before the use of the automatic radar range finder, it was necessary for the airman to adjust manually the circle and dot prior to firing the guns. The new gunsight is particularly effective at night or when daytime visibility is poor, simply because radar can "see" regardless of these conditions. American Sabre Jets in the Korean war were armed with this radar-electronic gunsight and blasted an overwhelming number of Migs out of the sky, close to a 13-to-1 ratio.

Now engineers are working on methods to make this electronic equipment even more perfect in performance. They are developing a unit which, when hooked up to a plane's automatic pilot, will seek out, fly to and fire upon the target automatically. When this device is perfected, the pilot's job will have been reduced for all practical purposes to that of an observer.

Since World War II radar-bombsights have been developed that far outstrip the early models. Although much secrecy still surrounds this equipment, the curtain has been lifted a bit on one device to give us some inkling of its nature. Identified as the K-1, the bombsight weighs about 1,700 pounds and is jammed with 365 vacuum tubes. Its cost has been estimated in the neighborhood of $200,000, which gives some idea of the complexity of present-day electronic fighting equipment.

The K-1 bombsight is said to operate pretty much on an automatic basis. It is hooked up and works in close harmony with a bombing plane's automatic navigation apparatus. The radar-bombsight enables a jet bomber speeding close to 600 miles an hour and at an altitude of better than 35,000 feet to drop its bombs with precision upon a target. Cloudy skies or the darkness of night are no barrier for a plane equipped with this electronic instrument. Its accuracy is said to be even better than the old wartime Norden optical bombsight, which was considered the best of its day. Limited to daytime use only, it allowed bombers to pick out ground targets from altitudes only half of those of which the radar type is capable and at far less speed. One major fault of the older unit was the need for bombers to make a long straight run over the target before releasing their destructive eggs. This made it easy for ground fire to draw aim on them. The new radar-bombsight eliminates this weakness.

Ground-based military radar no less than the airborne variety has shown the effects of postwar research. As knowledge concerning the behavior of electromagnetic waves increased, better antennas were designed and more powerful tubes created which made radar beams more accurate and their reflections stronger. A new type of radar has even been developed which picks up only moving objects on its scope. It is also capable of scanning lower altitude levels far more efficiently than older units. Equipped with a moving target indicator, this new radar apparatus is expected to provide an effective warning screen against low-flying hostile aircraft.

Other technical advances have increased the scanning ability of radar to the point where it can tell, in the case of airplanes

A typical radar unit of the United States Air Force on a mountain-top location during the Korean War. *Air Force Photo.*

with propellers, the number of motors powering them as well as their speed and location, all with great swiftness. Feeding this data continuously to electronic computers, which are becoming more and more an essential part of radar apparatus, these devices make detailed information about unfriendly planes instantly available to ground observers. One of the more striking developments connected with present-day radar concerns its almost completely automatic nature.

During the last world conflict it required a group of 300 men to run a radar ground installation properly. Now that scientists have found ways to make many of its functions self-operating, a complete station can be handled easily by eight men. One of the features which has helped to bring this about is a bell device attached to the radar scope. Every time a "pip" shows up, the bell rings and alerts an observer. This eliminates the tiring job of keeping an operator continuously before the indicator screen to watch for target signals. But even this small number of operators, it seems, will shortly be reduced on many types of radar units to zero. Radar sets are emerging from the laboratory that can operate entirely by themselves and require no human observers. The target data which they gather will be sent swiftly and automatically to distant central information points.

Automatic radar installations such as these, together with those requiring human attendants, are being used to form a fence of warning stations along the northern bounds of the American continent. Stretching from Alaska to Greenland and Alaska to Labrador, the double line of radar observation posts is expected to give ample warning of any hostile air force heading toward Canada and the United States from that direction. Smaller automatic radar sets are being erected to fill the gaps between the larger installations. Since they can function without human observers, automatic radar units will be ideal for the cold, barren land in which they will be set up.

A different type of radar equipment is being used to supplement the ground radar installations guarding the seacoasts of

A radar picket plane. Planes such as this are used by the U. S. Air Force and Navy for patrolling the off-shore coastal areas of the United States. Plane is capable of carrying a crew of 31, including relief pilots, radar officers, technicians and maintenance specialists. *Official U. S. Navy Photo.*

the United States. Long-range search aircraft both of the Air Force and Navy, known as picket patrol planes, are constantly scanning the skies and the seas with the latest in airborne radar-detecting apparatus. The majority of these are multi-engine craft, and just as with the early models that first appeared in the last war, the sleek lines of their fuselage are broken by awkward-looking bulges called radomes. These conceal sensitive radar antennas and reflectors and other electronic gear. Some radomes stick up vertically from the back of the planes like a funnel on a steamship; others are large, round bulging affairs fastened to the belly of the plane, looking much like the inflated throat of a bullfrog. The radomes are made of plastic, weigh very little and do not interfere with the passage of radar signals or echoes.

Not all of the latest radar military equipment being produced is restricted to use in hunting enemy airplanes or ships. The United States Army recently revealed that it has developed a unit for the benefit of the foot soldier. This detecting device is a mobile affair and is designed to be taken up to the front areas to guard against enemy soldiers infiltrating through defense lines at night. The radar unit can also be used for probing behind enemy lines to spot movements of supplies and troops.

Military equipment of present-day fighting forces, unlike that used by soldiers of other eras, is of a highly technical nature. Radar, with its very complex make-up, is one of the more important elements contributing to this modern military development. Skilled men are required both to operate it and to take care of the apparatus, especially when it doesn't function properly. To produce men capable of operating and maintaining the horde of complex devices used by the Navy, Army and Air Force, it has been necessary to establish new training procedures as well as to acquire novel instructional equipment. An interesting example of this was revealed by the United States Air Force not too long ago. Designed to help train aircraft crewmen in the use of radar, navigating, and bombing equipment, this apparatus will be used only for advanced training purposes of men who are already skilled in one of the three fields. It is intended to make one man an expert in all three categories so that in the future the Air Force will be able to reduce the size of its crews on long-range bombers.

Based on the principles of ultrasonic waves (sound waves far above the range of the human ear), this training apparatus consists of a make-believe airplane carrying all the airborne radar equipment and other vital flight instruments to be found in a present-day bomber. In its operation the trainer makes use of some fundamental facts of physics, such as the reflecting ability of both ultrasonic waves and electromagnetic waves. There is a difference between the two in that the radar signals travel with far greater speed, in the ratio of 200,000 to 1, when the medium of air and water are considered. Using this precise ratio as a base, it has been found that a make-believe radar flight can be achieved in a very accurate manner if an ultrasonic transmitting and receiving unit is moved over a scaled contour map of any particular portion of the earth. The trainer therefore makes use of a map scaled to 1/200,000 of the area of the globe it represents; this is submerged in a tank of purified water. The tem-

This huge tank is a part of the new device developed for the United States Air Forces for training navigators and bombardiers without the need of actual flight. Simplane (simulated airplane) moves over a submerged relief map giving navigator-bombardier trainee effect of a real flight over terrain represented by map. *American Machine & Foundry Company, Electronics Division.*

perature of the water is strictly controlled so that the scale of the map does not become distorted.

A crane assembly allows the make-believe airplane—called a "simplane"—to move above the pool of water containing the contour map. It also carries the antenna which, combined with the transmit-receive unit, is known as the "sontenna." The movement in effect simulates the flight of a bomber. The ultrasonic waves radiated through the water by the antenna strike various sections of the terrain map and are reflected, just like radar pulses, on a display screen before the student. In very realistic fashion, he sees an exact replica of a target area on a regular combat bombing mission. The training unit can also be employed to coach a student in the use of ground-based radar beacon signals for navigation purposes and acquaint him with radar jamming techniques. An instructor located at a special control board can create a variety of problems connected with both these subjects for a trainee to solve. Plotting boards record how well a student is reacting to the radar, bombing and navigating questions put before him.

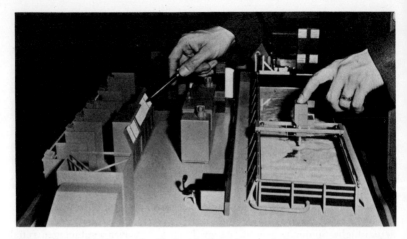

This scale model shows the U. S. Air Force's new radar trainer for navigators and bombardiers. At left are plotting boards which record the course flown, bomb fall and hit accuracy. At right is the simplane which moves over a special map submerged in a shallow tank of water. In the center is the control board where instructor-director sets up the flight problem. To the far left are booths for the multiple training of air crew personnel. *American Machine & Foundry Company, Electronics Division.*

This newly developed radar trainer can thoroughly acquaint bomber crews with flying problems in any portion of the world without their leaving the ground in the United States.

Another radar device of a similar nature has also been acquired by the Air Force. This apparatus is called a "Navascreen" and is used for studying air traffic problems over airports. It consists of a large screen somewhat like that seen in motion picture theaters. This is translucent in nature and on it paths of thirteen make-believe airplanes can be projected. These correspond to the "pips" picked up on a real radar scope. Thirteen control cabinets are stationed before the screen operated by thirteen "pilots" who can regulate the speed and direction of the "planes" on the screen. Each aircraft shows up as a small dot of light.

An air traffic controller can regulate the course, speed, and altitude of these various make-believe planes as they hover over a pre-selected airport area. This is also projected on the screen and can represent any airfield in the world. A great variety of congested landing conditions can be simulated and their solutions worked out by the grounded "pilots." New radar methods of reducing these problems can also be studied by the use of "Navascreen."

Radar was first applied to aircraft navigation in World War II, when the sky was literally filled with swarms of fighting craft zooming back and forth between bases and targets. Although conventional maritime guidance methods were commonly used, they often proved inadequate, especially when the weather suddenly took a turn for the worse. This frequently happened as fleets of bombers headed for home after flying hundreds of miles to an objective. Some better system was needed if airmen were to be prevented from missing their home ports. As a result electronic scientists and engineers developed the radar beacon. This operated much like the beam of light from a lighthouse, except that it radiated a continuous series of radio signals which flyers picked up on their receivers and which guided them to their goal.

This wartime radar beacon guidance system was effective, but left plenty of room for improvement. One weakness was the lengthy period of time it took a crew to translate the signals into the desired navigation information. Not long after the conclusion of World War II a better method was devised, known as Distance Measuring Equipment or DME for short. Both the military services in the United States and the research laboratory of the International Telephone and Telegraph Corporation joined forces in bringing this improved radar guidance system into existence.

DME is a combination of ground and airborne radar. The ground unit is still called a beacon and, just as with the set aboard the airplane, it can transmit radar pulses and receive them. With this new system, the transmitter aboard the airplane starts the operation for obtaining a distance measurement by

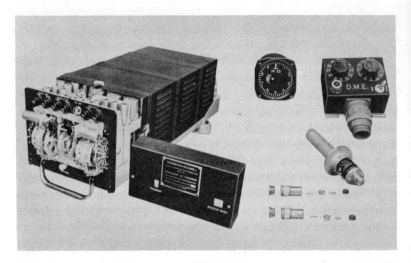

Distance measuring Equipment—DME, developed in collaboration with the U. S. Government by I. T. & T.'s central laboratory in the United States, is a combination of ground and airborne radar. The new aid gives the pilot of an airplane his speed in relation to the ground and, like the mileage indicator in an automobile, tells him precisely how far he has progressed to or from a known geographical point, usually an omnirange radio station. *I. T. & T.*

sending out radar pulses. Special channels are used for these transmitted pulses to which both the airplane and ground beacon are tuned. When the ground radar station receives the challenging pulse, it responds by sending a similar one to the aircraft. A receiver unit on the plane takes the beacon pulse and, through a complicated electronic hook-up, measures the time that has elapsed between the transmitted pulse and the response pulse. An electronic computer or "brain" takes over at this point and converts this time element into a numerical term so the pilot knows exactly how far he is from the ground beacon. The operation of the equipment is a continuous one so the pilot has up-to-the minute information at all times.

The distance-indicator is a simple affair, clock-like in appearance and equipped with a pointer. This spins around on a calibrated face that runs from 0 to 100 nautical miles which is the approximate range of the guidance system. The radar beacon uses an antenna described as an omni-directional type. This means that it radiates its signals in all directions in a horizontal plane. The beacon also flashes a vertical beam that spans a path about 10° wide. Fifty aircraft can make use of its guidance signals at a time. Since DME's debut, it has proved highly accurate and extremely helpful in navigation not only to military aircraft but to commercial planes as well.

A long-range navigation system, a variation of DME, is now under development by both this same private research laboratory and technical military groups in the United States and is called Navaglobe. Three radar beacons are used with this navigational aid which are accurately positioned in the form of an equilateral triangle on the ground. First they send out signals separately and then as a unit, all within a span of one second. A receiver aboard the plane picks up the pulses and by means of complicated electronic devices automatically converts them into numerical terms showing the plane's location in relation to the three beacons. Navaglobe is said to have a range of a little more than 1,500 miles.

Airports, whether military or civil, can present a confused sight during periods of peak operations. Planes leaving parking areas for runways, others coming in from landing strips can present pretty much of a jumble, dangerous not only to personnel handling them but also to the aircraft themselves. This is especially true at night or when visibility is poor. The Air Force was keenly aware of this difficulty from its experience during World War II at airfields busy with the coming and going of hundreds of fighter and bomber planes. During the postwar years the problem was handed over to their research and development laboratories, who came up with a solution involving radar. The unit is called Airport Surface Detection Equipment, or more popularly taxi radar.

The equipment consists of a conventional radar set that can detect objects at very close range with extreme accuracy. Planes

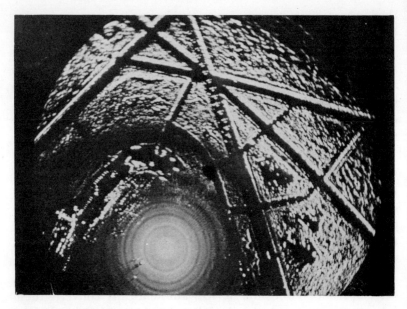

A busy airport's runways and terminal area as shown on the scope of the newly developed Taxi Radar. *U. S. Air Force.*

which are picked up on its scope as they leave the runways or parking area at the terminal building, even have their wings and tail surfaces clearly defined. Variations in shading of grass and shrubs are also easily recognized on the taxi radar's screen. The antenna is normally located on the highest point available at whatever field it is used, in many cases, the control tower. While radiating and receiving radar signals, the antenna rotates sixty times a minute, which is an important feature of its sensitive detecting ability.

For a whole year this surface radar detector was tried out at New York's International Airport, where it proved extremely successful. Operators of the unit were able to guide moving airplanes to their proper places as well as to check on the movements of trucks and other vehicles.

Still another radar aid for controlling air traffic at a busy airport is an experimental unit produced for the Air Force showing airplanes in two colors on the scope. Since the war it has become a common practice for airplanes using radar guidance into airfields to respond to a radar signal from the ground with one of their own. This is registered on the scope and is known as an artificial echo. It is used primarily because it makes for a brighter, stronger "pip" which is a help to the airport traffic controller. In the conventional radar equipment where responder signals are used, the second echo is picked up on another scope instead of the one for the natural echo. This task also requires a second antenna. The new experimental two-color system eliminates much of this additional equipment.

Instead of showing the two different "pips" on separate scopes, they are superimposed at the same spot, corresponding to the plane's location, on a single scope. The observer may distinguish between the natural and artificial echoes, since they appear in contrasting colors. Furthermore, only a single antenna is needed to pick up the two echoes.

Since World War II, scientists and engineers have been working to perfect still further GCA, the bad weather airport traffic control system. Their efforts have been fruitful. GCA has been improved since the war years so that it is now capable of detecting airplanes as high as 10,000 feet and as far distant as 50 miles. Formerly the maximum limits were 4,000 feet and 18 miles. One man can now operate this blind landing system while bringing in three planes at one time, whereas during the war a 5-man crew was needed to land just one aircraft at a time. The number of scopes has also been reduced from 6 to 2. Important from the military standpoint has been the reduction in the equipment's bulk so that today it can be packed in a cargo plane and hauled away over long distances. Older units were housed in 22-ton trailer trucks. Most important of all, GCA has been brought to the stage where it can automatically guide a plane almost to the point of touchdown on a runway. Still largely experimental, this new apparatus is known as Automatic Ground Control Approach.

Mobile units used with GCA blind landing system. *Gilfillan Bros., Inc.*

The modern airplane, both military and civilian, is a complex vehicle to operate. It requires a man with swift reflexes and a trigger-quick mind to cope with the mass of complicated but vital instruments and devices that surround a pilot in the cockpit. This is a formidable task while the weather is good, but it becomes doubly so when the pilot is groping his way through clouds or fog. During those moments he is relying largely on the information of his instruments and the help of his electronic equipment. However, the time is rapidly approaching, with the constant addition of new electronic devices to airplanes, when the pilot is beginning to feel overwhelmed by them. He is finding it more and more difficult to match his own mental and physical abilities with theirs. Many pilots have said that even now, they experience moments when the electronic apparatus appears too much to handle. This is especially so when they are making a landing on instruments, such as with the help of GCA. As a consequence much of the electronic apparatus being created today for aviation is becoming increasingly self-operating to relieve the pilot of many of his strenuous flying chores. The Automatic Ground Control Approach system promises to be a big step in that direction.

Laboratories of private industry as well as those of the government have pooled their scientific and engineering talents to bring this unique apparatus into existence. With uncanny accuracy and swiftness, it can pick out an airplane nearing an airport with its "all-seeing" radar eye, lock its electronic hands on the plane's autopilot and guide it along the proper glide path to within several feet of the runway before the pilot need take over the controls. Its ability is such that it can bring six airplanes down the runway approach-point simultaneously at one minute intervals.

The new equipment consists of a standard GCA radar unit plus an electronic brain that actually flies the airplane down through its correct landing glide. In order for a pilot to make use of this ground guidance system, he first must call the control

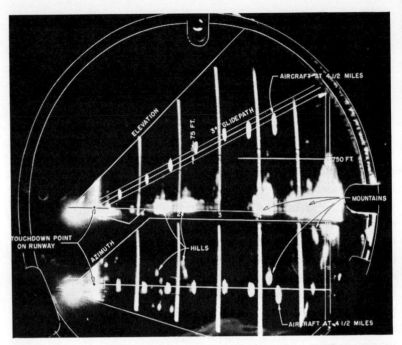

This is what an airport controller sees on a Precision Approach Radar Screen which has a range of about 10 miles. The upper portion gives the elevation picture; the lower gives the azimuth picture. The vertical lines give the distance in miles from touchdown point and are spaced 1 mile apart. Aircraft being radar guided in this view are already on the glide path leading to runwav. *Gilfillan Bros., Inc.*

tower at an airfield. Operators here clear his request and tell him to actuate his airborne portion of AGCA equipment. The pilot proceeds to push a button on his instrument panel which flashes a signal to the ground radar unit. Automatically this device goes into action guiding the incoming airplane into its proper landing pattern, just as human operators would do using conventional GCA equipment.

Among its numerous self-operating electronic features are those designed to make it as foolproof as possible. One of the most important of these can tell when the airplane is not in the correct approach position for meeting the runway. Should this happen, the electronic brain quickly and automatically warns the pilot of the condition and signals him to fly away for another try at the approach.

So far AGCA has undergone exhaustive tests involving hundreds of flights. These have not only helped technicians to remove the "bugs" that usually show up in experimental apparatus, but also to prove the basic value of the system itself. Some day when AGCA reaches the ultimate in its development, planes will be guided all the way down to a runway and stopped automatically.

Still another version of a ground-control landing system combining radar and electronic tracking and computer units has been developed for the U. S. Air Force called "Volscan." This electronic guidance equipment is said to be capable of landing 120 planes an hour, about four times faster than by other methods.

The United States Navy is utilizing radar to help land speedy jet planes on the decks of aircraft carriers. This maneuver, involving a fast plane and a moving ship, is often hazardous. If the plane's speed is too great, it will miss the arresting cables or overshoot the deck completely. On the other hand, if the plane's velocity is too low, it may stall in midair and drop into the water.

The aircraft carrier radar landing equipment is a speed measuring device that tracks incoming aircraft. Other elements in the apparatus find out the true speed of an approaching plane and coordinate its velocity with the speed of the carrier and of the prevailing wind. The last two factors are important for helping a pilot maintain the correct landing speed. The data which the radar speed measuring device gathers is shown on a meter mounted to a carrier's deck at the place occupied by the Landing Signal Officer. By watching this meter, this officer can tell whether an approaching plane is traveling too fast or too slowly and thus guide the pilot in for a landing or wave him off

TRODI (Touchdown Rate of Descent Indicator) shown here on deck of aircraft carrier USS *Midway,* is used by the Navy to determine quickly the proper speed at which a plane must descend to make a safe carrier landing. *North American Aviation.*

to make another try. The radar carrier landing equipment is expected to be particularly helpful for Naval flyers when the weather is unfavorable.

Although not strictly radar equipment, a somewhat similar instrument has also been developed called TRODI (Touch down Rate of Descent Indicator). Trodi sends out two beams of light through which the approaching plane must pass. An electronic circuit within the equipment is set in action and this determines quickly the proper speed at which the plane must descend to make a safe carrier landing. An electronic instrument such as this is especially valuable when a new model jet plane is being adapted for carrier operations.

Peacetime Radar

Up to now we have discussed only those military radar developments that could be applied for some wartime purpose. But shortly after the close of World War II, a radar achievement took place which, although of less immediate practical usefulness, was of great scientific significance. This was the Army Signal Corps' experiment in contacting the moon by radar. The historic event took place on January 10, 1946.

Scientists connected with the Signal Corps' electronic research laboratory had long been intrigued with the notion of some day shooting radar pulses to the moon. This idea was born during the pioneering era when the first workable radar apparatus was being developed. The war interfered with the plans, but, just as soon as the conflict ended, they made preparations to carry it out. Two questions had to be answered before they could expect any measure of success. Could electromagnetic waves be developed of sufficiently high frequency to allow them to travel the vast empty void separating the earth and the moon—about 238,857 miles? Further, they had to find out whether it would be possible for these radiating frequencies to penetrate through the ionosphere, the electrified atmosphere layer that envelops our earth. Many scientists had their doubts about this last point, but those at the Signal Corps Laboratory were not satisfied until they made the attempt.

Preparations for the experiment were begun weeks in advance, with physicists and mathematicians working on endless figures to determine with extreme accuracy when the earth and the moon would be in the most favorable position. They had to calculate precisely the speed of the moon in relation to that of the earth. Meanwhile other scientists began designing and building the equipment that would be used.

This is the huge radar antenna used for radar-to-the-moon experiments. *Official U. S. Navy Photo.*

The radar set, with modifications of course, was one that they had designed back in 1937 for long-range detection against enemy air attack. The power which the set generated was not changed, but the form of the pulse signal was. Instead of sending out several thousand spaced pulses each second, the radar unit flashed a super-powerful pulse every five seconds. The time of each pulse was also increased from a few billionths of a second to about a half-second. In other words, the enormous amount of radio energy generated for the pulse lasted for about a half-second at every five-second period of transmission.

The scope used on this moon radar set was of the A-type, but it was changed in such a way that an echo signal which it registered would last longer and be of greater brilliance than those on conventional screens. A special antenna-reflector assembly was also constructed. This consisted of a 100-foot tower topped by a double-size rectangular shaped reflector, which was aimed at the moon by a specially built optical sighting instrument called a peepsight. The scientists had to exercise particular care with this radar set because of the huge amounts of electrical energy generated. The vacuum tubes had to be water-cooled to prevent the transmitter from burning out.

On the night of January 10 everything was finally in order for the experiment. Soon the first of a series of powerful radio pulses went surging on its way through space. An electronic light beam or sweep began making its way across the face of the tube showing the transit of the successive pulses. Two and a half seconds from the time the first pulse waves were flashed to the moon, echo "pips" appeared on the radar scope. In that brief span of time the electrified ionosphere curtain had been pierced, the moon struck with a radar pulse and the return trip to the transmitter completed. Although it took several days to verify the data which they had obtained, the Signal Corps scientists were nevertheless jubilant with their accomplishment. They had not only solved two scientific puzzles, but demonstrated in spectacular fashion a new tool for those working in the field of pure research.

Radar is proving itself no less valuable in the more peaceful pursuits of life than in those of war. Just as soon as the military monopoly on radar equipment was relaxed at the end of World War II, scientists and engineers lost little time in adapting it for peacetime purposes. And just as with radar's wartime history, it found its widest application in the field of transportation—in the air, on the sea and on land.

We have already seen how military planes have utilized certain radar devices for guidance and navigation purposes. This same equipment with very little alteration has been made available for commercial planes. GCA, for example, is installed at practically all the major airfields throughout the world to help

The CAA Air Route Traffic Control Center at Washington National, one of 31 such installations around the country, is a busy place in instrument weather. *CAA Photo.*

Radar operator in control tower at CAA's Washington National Airport scans precision approach radar scope. *CAA Photo.*

passenger airliners make safe landings in bad weather. Distance Measuring Equipment, together with radar beacons, is also helping commercial airline pilots to find their way from airport to airport, faster and more accurately than ever before.

With passenger planes increasing in number, complexity and

speed, the pilot's job, as we have stated, is rapidly approaching the superhuman stage. Jet airliners with speeds of five hundred and six hundred miles an hour, now appearing on commercial air routes, are not making his lot an easier one. With these speed demons of the skyways, the pilot must know, more than ever before, of obstructions in his line of flight, not only in the form of other aircraft or mountains, but of storm clouds as well, since these usually gather about seething masses of violent air currents. A plane flying through such centers would experience all sorts of stresses, far greater perhaps than it was designed to take. This might result, of course, in a fatal crash. Because of the high velocity of modern planes, the pilot must be alerted to such dangers while they are still some distance away.

New aids are therefore constantly being developed to ease the burden of commercial pilots still further. A recently created anti-collision radar unit is expected to provide a continuous picture of obstacles in the line of flight, whether at night, during bad weather, or even, if necessary, when the weather is fair. The device is light and small enough to be carried aboard a plane along with other navigation equipment. It operates just like standard radar units with its pulsed radar beam, which is sufficiently powerful to detect storm cloud formations 40,000 feet high and at a distance of forty miles. One version of this radar equipment, produced in England, is getting a tryout on a new jet passenger plane of the British Overseas Airways. Similar units are under development in the United States, and as evidence of their progress, Pan American Airways is installing airborne radar units on its passenger planes flying the South American routes. The radar equipment will warn air crews of bad flying weather up to 100 miles ahead. Safer and more comfortable air travel is expected as a result.

Radar is equally important, if not more so, to ocean liners as to airliners. In the goal of greater safety for ships at sea, radar has proved second, perhaps, only to radio communication, facilitating navigation and helping the crew to foresee obstacles on their course. And marine radar equipment, like that being adapted for aircraft, is constantly appearing in new and more efficient forms. One of the latest is the Powergraph Position Tracker.

This radar device permits navigators aboard ship not only to see objects at night or in bad weather, but also, in the case of other moving vessels, to plot their path directly onto the radar scope itself. Thus the navigator has a constant record of the other ship's course in relation to his own—whether boats are maintaining their proper distance, converging or drawing away from each other. When a ship is required to sail rather close to the coastline, the Position Tracker gives the navigator a continuous check on whether he is maintaining the proper distance from land.

This Powergraph Position Tracker is an attachment that fastens over the face of the radar scope. It consists of a concave glass having a surface that can easily be written upon and a special kind of two-color mirror, called dichroic. Sandwiched between the true face of the radar scope and the outer concave glass shield, this mirror has the unusual ability of reflecting down on the face of the scope any wax pencil mark made on the concave glass. The reflected mark is shown in red on the face of the radar screen.

But the mirror does more than this. The normal yellow spot of light, the target "pip" that appears on the scope, can show through the mirror to the eye of an observer. The position of a target or targets can therefore be recorded directly on the outer concave glass. Every time the targets change position, new pencil recordings are made, giving an accurate up-to-the-minute picture of the relative position of the radar objects to the ship. Previous methods used for plotting the course of radar targets called for bulky equipment which meant that the navigator needed considerable time to obtain his desired information. Now, with a flick of a switch on a small, compact cabinet which houses the radar receiver, a navigator using a few pencil marks can see instantly the nature of the traffic in the region of his vessel.

Not all the marine radar equipment, however, is intended for shipboard use. Ramark, for example, is an experimental radar beacon buoy which the United States Coast Guard is develop-

A buoy radar reflector being developed by the United States Coast Guard. *Official Coast Guard Photo.*

ing. Ramark (the name is derived from the words, radar marked beacon) is not much different in appearance from a normal channel buoy except that it has a built-in radar transmitter. This unit sends out a radar pulse in a continuous pattern on a certain frequency. A ship's radar receiver can pick up the beacon pulse if it is tuned to the same frequency used by the buoy transmitter.

The beacon pulse registers on the radar scope as a pencil-thin beam of light. This radiates from the center of the screen to the outer edge, its position corresponding to the direction of the buoy from the ship itself. Since the scope is scaled in degrees, the position of the sweep enables the navigator to obtain his bearing quickly. Incidentally, bearing information is all that Ramark can provide a navigator. However, by using the pulses from two separately located radar marker beacons, the navigator can also find his exact location. Ramark is expected to be especially helpful in giving ships their bearing at night or during periods of fog.

Still another innovation is being contemplated for marker buoys, particularly those used in channels, to help make a ship's radar equipment more effective. Reflector attachments are being added to the tops of buoys so that they will throw back a stronger echo to a ship's receiver. These are built in the shape of a corner, which gives them their name of corner reflectors. As a ship's radar beam picks up the reflector, a pulse hits one side of the corner, bounces off another and then out to the boat's radar antenna. Maritime authorities both in this country and Europe are experimenting with these buoy radar reflectors.

Ships that sail the ocean lanes are not alone in making good use of radar's all-seeing "eye." Smaller boats, like tugs and

Radar scope inside tugboat pilot room. *The New Haven Railroad.*

ferries that work in busy harbors, have found radar equally valuable. This is especially true when a harbor is shrouded in fog. Then the radio detecting equipment permits boats to sail practically as usual throughout the harbor area without danger of bumping into other boats. Towboats that push tons of cargo along the inland rivers of the United States also make use of radar's uncanny detecting ability. Channel markers or obstructions in the river are clearly picked up on the scope and revealed to a captain at night and in bad visibility.

Ocean-going passenger vessels usually operate on a very precise schedule. It is important from a money-making angle for a boat to tie up to a pier after reaching its destination, unload quickly, take on new passengers and cargo, and depart. It often happens that when an ocean liner is about to make port, some adverse weather condition, usually fog, forces it to anchor out in a channel and delay its arrival. Even though a ship may have its own radar apparatus, this situation still arises. Normally the radar antenna on an ocean-going vessel is placed at the highest possible point so that the beam can spot objects at sea at the furthest distance. The area immediately in front of the ship is,

The Mariners' Pathfinder* is another of the newly developed radar units that permits the plotting of targets directly upon the glass surface above the PPI-scope. A parallax-correcting device makes this possible. *Ratheon Manufacturing Company.* * Reg. Trade Mark.

A radar set for use aboard small boats newly developed by the Decca Navigational Aid Company of England. No larger than an ordinary radio receiver, the marine radar unit has a 5-inch cathode-ray tube and a range from ½ to 25 miles. *British Information Service.*

however, a blind spot to the radar beam. Since harbor targets are almost all at very close range, the steamship cannot make full use of its detecting equipment.

This problem is now being solved by land-based radar installations located at strategic points around a harbor, but particularly at the entrance. Operating in much the same way as the blind landing system for airplanes, the shore-based radar observer "talks" the pilot of the ocean liner to his berth. With the help of two-way radio, he can tell the pilot of the incoming ship when boats are crossing his path or moving down the channel in an opposite direction. Aside from their guidance value, these radar lookout posts can also spot accidents occurring in channels during bad visibility and order help rushed to the scene. Several harbors in the United States and Europe, notably those of Los Angeles and Brest, France, have installations of this type.

To those who make their living from the products of the sea, whalers and fishing fleets particularly, radar has served other purposes than guidance alone. They use the radiating reflecting pulses to spot schools of fish and whales. In both these hazardous occupations radar has to some extent removed the element of "chance," while serving also in its more conventional way as a safety device.

Whaling activity today is a far cry from the rugged days when sailing ships were used. Now an entire fleet takes part in the operation, a mother ship and several smaller hunter boats. The mother ship is really a floating factory where the whales brought in by the smaller boats are processed. After the whaling fleet has reached the hunting grounds, the most popular of which are in the Antarctic region, the hunter boats scatter in all directions. They are equipped with two-way radio as well as radar and can keep in touch with one another and the mother ship. The mother ship also carries radar equipment, mainly for guiding the smaller boats back to their base in the event fog suddenly drops a blinding shroud over the sea. Radar on the hunter boats is used to scan the surrounding seas for whales, but also at night and during bad weather to warn of ice floes or other boats coming too close.

After a whale has been caught, it is killed and then inflated with compressed air to keep the carcass afloat. A steel reflector rod is jammed into the whale's body, which is temporarily abandoned as the hunter boat goes after others that might be in the vicinity. Later that same boat, or another, can locate the dead whale with radar, pick it up again, and tow it to the factory ship. Those who make their living at this dangerous job are said to be enthusiastic about the way radar has lightened their tasks.

Commercial fishing fleets are also finding radar a boon to the success of their operations, especially in helping to locate schools of fish. Actually the devices which they use are based on ultrasonics and are a variation of Sonar. These send out sound waves beneath the sea and, striking an underwater object, are reflected back to a receiver aboard ship. By watching the scope of his underwater radar unit, a fishing captain can tell if he is near

97

a school of fish. A remarkable instrument of this kind recently developed is known as the Fischlupe or Fish Finder.

Fischlupe originated in Germany. Its name is a combination of the German *Fisch,* and *lupe,* a French word meaning a small magnifying glass like that used by jewelers. This electronic apparatus is capable of scanning the ocean bottom with such accuracy that it not only can detect schools of fish but also identify varieties and even pick out a single fish. In addition, it is able to tell of conditions existing on the ocean floor and warn of underwater obstacles on which nets might become snagged.

The Fischlupe provides a constant view of underwater conditions to an effective depth of 1,680 feet. It sends powerful, fast-moving signals beneath the water, which, on striking the sea bottom or any objects in their path, are reflected back to the ship. This is the same basic method used by radar to pick up objects in the air. The echoes might be those of the ocean floor, rocks, wrecks, or a school of fish and show as light reflections on the face of a cathode-ray tube. This indicator face is marked with a calibrated scale that tells the fisherman how deep the object is that is sending back the echo. The light reflections show up as short, horizontal patterns.

When a school of fish is detected, the fisherman can obtain an enlarged view by using a range control switch which gives him a 48-foot vertical close-up section of the underwater area being scanned. This enlarged section can be moved anywhere within the maximum range of the detecting unit. By its use, the fisherman can obtain an accurate measurement of the depth and mass of a school of fish.

Fischlupe was first tried in America in the fall of 1953 and performed with astonishing results. The skipper on whose boat it was used reported that with its help he could tell the difference between hard and soft underwater bottom, between large and small haddock and that he could even distinguish haddock from cod.

Still another new device for underwater detection is called

the Echograph. It operates on the same basic echo-sounding principles as Fischlupe but provides a permanent picture of the underwater area it is exploring. This information is placed on electrosensitive dry recording paper 8" wide. It is valuable to the fisherman because it preserves data that he can use when he returns to a rich fishing ground.

Railroads have been among the first of the major land transportation fields to find a practical use for radar. Engineers connected with railroad operations have developed a device for use in classification yards that warn when freight cars are moving too fast to be hitched onto trains. When trains are made up in classification yards, freight cars are pushed over a low rise in the ground by a switching engine and then left to roll by gravity to join a string of other cars. The trouble with this method is that sometimes cars roll downhill too fast and make coupling to others a dangerous job. The radar speed meter is helping to guard against this difficulty.

The main portion of this detecting equipment is fixed to a pole and erected in a strategic spot in the classification yard. As the freight cars roll by, they trigger the radar beam if their speed is above normal. This causes a signal to be flashed to an operator in a control tower in the freight yard. The operator quickly puts certain electronic units in operation that cause special braking devices to slow the car down before it slams into the others.

This railroad radar equipment works on somewhat different principles from that of more conventional apparatus. The latter transmits radio waves in the form of powerful pulses, whereas the radar speed meter radiates waves in a steady stream whose characteristics are affected by changes in its frequencies. The equipment used by highway patrolmen to check on the speed of motorists is also based on this method of radiating radio waves.

The guard or sentry house is a common sight these days not only at military reservations but also at many of the country's

An electronic "cop" which operates similar to radar, is here warning of an approaching automobile. *General Electric Co.*

industrial plants. This is especially true if the latter are engaged in making war equipment. The job of keeping away unwanted visitors frequently becomes tiring and boring, with the result that guards after a while lose some of their alertness. Their attention can also be diverted elsewhere, making it possible for a person to slip by undetected. A sentry radar has now been developed to help them in their security assignment.

The equipment for this electronic cop consists of an 18-inch saucer-shaped antenna assembly mounted in such a way that the radar beam which it transmits covers the area in front of the guard house. When an approaching car or person intercepts the beam, an echo is reflected to the saucer antenna. The returning echo, unlike that of conventional radar, travels a zigzag course through the outgoing signals. From the antenna it passes to a special electronic hook-up that transforms the echo in such a way as to make it ring a bell inside the guard house. Thus, if a guard is momentarily relaxing or has his attention focused in another direction, the radar sentry alerts him to the oncoming visitor. The unit is also said to have a practical use for toll col-

This radar equipment is used by the United States Air Force for the detection of approaching storms. *Air Force Photo.*

lectors on super-highways and at entrances to tunnels and bridges.

One of the more interesting civil applications of radar concerns its connection with meteorological problems. Not only is it being used to help provide conventional weather information but special types of radar apparatus have also been created to warn of more violent conditions such as hurricanes and tornadoes. Tornadoes commonly occur in the midwestern part of the United States. Each year they exact an enormous toll in lives lost and property damage. After every such disaster there is a rash of suggestions for guarding against them, ranging from constructing giant underground shelters to exploding an A-bomb to divert the furious air currents. But most of these never progress further than the talking stage, and the danger continues. The exception is a recently announced radar warning system developed by Dr. H. L. Jones, of Oklahoma A. & M.

College. It holds great promise of reducing, if not eliminating, the death toll caused by tornadoes.

It took Dr. Jones six years to develop this device. He started with a theory that tornadoes eject a peculiar type of electrical charge that makes them different from other kinds of weather disturbances. His first and important job then was to prove his theory, which he did. He found that tornadoes radiate a high-voltage discharge identified as sferics. He also determined the number of times these discharges or lightning strokes usually occur during a storm and their duration. After this it was a case of building the proper radar equipment that could register these storm characteristics on a scope.

As finally assembled, Dr. Jones' tornado radar warning equipment consists of four basic items. These are a normal radar unit, a direction-finding apparatus, a wave form analyzer, and a complex electronic unit consisting of an oscilloscope, among other things, capable of transforming the high-voltage discharges of the tornado into visible lines. One final piece of equipment in the warning system has the long-winded name of "storm intensity incident azimuth intergrator," or, as it is better known, a tornado meter.

Dr. Jones' tornado warning system first locates an approaching storm by means of the radar unit. The oscilloscope, which operates like a TV tube, picks up the high-voltage discharges to see if tornado characteristics are present. Working closely with the oscilloscope, the direction-finder helps to plot the course of the swiftly moving storm. The tornado meter, though the last of the units to go into action performs not the least of the system's functions, actually measuring the storm by degree of intensity.

This intensity gauge is really the key to the effectiveness of tornado-warning apparatus. According to Dr. Jones, when the meter indicates the occurrence of fifteen lightning strokes or sferics a second, it means that a heavy hail shower is pelting the earth and that the storm has tornado-building tendencies. When the number of lightning strokes reaches twenty-three a second, the storm is busy creating tornado winds. At 26 sferics a second, a tornado is actually in progress and its destructive winds are beginning to move across the countryside.

A nationwide warning system of this type, the inventor admits, would be an expensive undertaking but far cheaper than the sum of property damage that these storms inflict. Its value, of course, cannot even be assessed against the human lives that would in all likelihood be saved. Either state governments or the federal government would have to undertake the construction and operation of such a warning system. According to Dr. Jones, a station manned by a crew of six would cost in the neighborhood of $300,000. He believes that 50 to 100 warning stations would be needed to cover thoroughly the area usually visited by tornadoes.

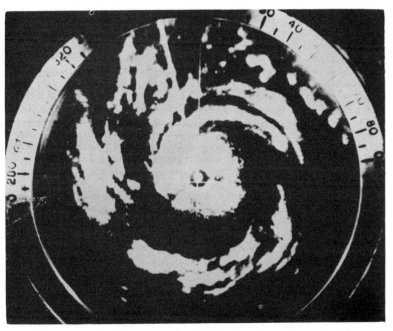

Looking at the "eye" of a hurricane. Note the spiral formation of the storm clouds. *Air Force Photo.*

Hurricanes, which frequently have their origin in the southern regions of the Caribbean Sea before roaring northward to the mainland of the United States, have long been traced down by Air Force planes with airborne radar equipment. Flying into the teeth of these howling tempests, the hurricane warning planes determine the velocity of the winds and the most likely route of the storm. Coupling this information with that obtained by ground weather stations, hurricane warnings are now given well in advance of their arrival.

Radar's possibilities for advancing weather knowledge are also being vigorously investigated by scientists and engineers in England. They have recently come up with a radar technique that permits them to gather important weather information from an altitude of more than twenty miles. Electronic recording units are fastened to hydrogen-filled balloons and sent aloft. As the balloons and their cargo soar higher and higher into the sky, a radar tracking device keeps them in view and also maintains contact with them by pulse signals. The transmitter attached to the balloons sends back their replies in the form of pulses which are received by the radar ground stations.

Data picked up by the electronic recorders and sent back to earth include such items as wind velocity, temperature, barometric pressure and humidity. Information of this kind about the higher altitude regions is a big help to meteorologists in making more accurate future weather predictions. This English-built radar tracking unit can spot weather balloons twenty miles high and more than 100 miles away. Knowledge of weather conditions at these heights is also important for jet flyers who normally travel several miles above the earth.

Radar in terms of years is a mere youth. Despite its brief history, however, it has already shown extraordinary versatility in its benefits to mankind. Few dare to predict how this versatility will increase in the future, but already there are signs of its far-reaching potentialities. Who would say, ten years ago, that radar might some day serve a specialized task in the medical world? Yet that is precisely what radar promises to do in the very near future. Several devices now under development are expected to be of considerable value in man's fight against one of the most baffling and dreaded diseases to which he is prey—cancer. One of the more interesting of these units is the work of Dr. D. H. Howdry of the University of Colorado who calls his radar medical apparatus a Somascope.

The Somascope, which Dr. Howdry has had under development for six years, uses a thin stream of ultra-high sound waves which probe and picture on a TV screen the internal soft organs of the human body. This type of medical examination is beyond the scope of ordinary X-rays. The machine is said to be capable of "seeing" internal malignant growth and even distinguishing among certain types. The device uses both ultrasonics and more conventional radar methods to accomplish its task.

First, ultra-high sound waves on the order of 1,000,000 cycles a second are created. These are produced by the electrical vibrations of a crystal of quartz or barium titanate. Sounds of this high frequency cannot be heard, nor can they travel through the air. Therefore the patient being examined by the machine is partly submerged in water while the sound-producing crystal is submerged completely. The ultrasonic beam is about one-sixteenth of an inch in diameter as it travels through the human body.

When the high-frequency stream, similar to radar radio waves, strikes an organ, it sends back an echo. The echo flashes to a receiver where it is transformed into electric impulses and then moves onto a television screen. As the ultrasonic beam explores the patient's suspected diseased organ, the resulting echoes trace an outline of the subject on the TV screen. Dr. Howdry calls the TV pictures "Somagrams." He feels that once his radar Somascope is perfected, it should help doctors in their study of illnesses affecting the liver, pancreas, stomach, and intestines.

The usefulness of radar appears infinite in range, limited only by the imagination and technical genius of modern man.

Chapter Four

ELECTRONICS AT WORK

During World War II military demands for new and more effective fighting equipment provided a powerful stimulant to the progress of electronics. Scientists and engineers in the field responded to the urgent need with truly amazing electronic devices and apparatus, many of which contributed to the successful outcome of specific military campaigns. Impressed with its wartime achievements, the armed forces of the United States and other nations continue to encourage the development of even more fantastic electronic equipment. Much of this is hidden behind a necessary curtain of secrecy, but enough has been revealed to give us a pretty good idea of an ever-growing role of electronics in military affairs.

Ground Training for Pilots

We have seen how the training of airmen in the handling of present-day high-speed planes depends heavily on electronics.

A close-up of the jet plane trainer's control panel. *Link Aviation, Inc.*

Modern aircraft, particularly the jet types, are complex vehicles which present increasing difficulties in training a man to fly them without endangering either himself or expensive equipment. The answer to this training dilemma has been the creation of electronic Flight Simulators.

Flight Simulators are exact representations of the cockpit of a particular type of airplane such as an advanced trainer, jet fighter, or even a four-motored transport. They duplicate instrument equipment and controls just as they exist on a real airplane. These are operated by electronic and mechanical means. As the pilot operates controls governing the movement of ailerons, rudder, flaps, throttle and the many other devices required to fly an airplane, these actions are translated into instrument panel readings with the help of electronic computers. The electronic brains are usually located outside the training cockpit. They indicate to the airman on his make-believe flight

This flight simulator is one of the latest used by the U. S. Air Force for the training of jet pilots. Its equipment is such that it allows a trainee to become familiar with the newest instruments and radio navigation systems as well as to gain experience in meeting all possible flight emergencies. *Link Aviation, Inc.*

Pilot's compartment in Flight Simulator duplicates exactly the controls and instruments found in a real airplane. *Curtiss-Wright Corp., Electronics Div.*

his rate of turn, rate of climb, air-speed and the like. The simulators provide an uncanny feeling of real flying.

These mock aircraft also increase the sensation of reality by vibration, engine noises, if it is a prop-driven replica, and even the hiss of air flowing over the top and along the sides as in an airborne plane. As a final touch, they duplicate the sound of screeching tires as they touch down on a runway.

One of the most important additional features of these simulators is that they allow experienced airmen to keep their skill in meeting certain emergencies while flying. All pilots, both military and commercial, are trained to cope with a number of dangerous possibilities in flight. Naturally hazards do not always arise in everyday flying. As a result, airmen tend to lose practice in instantaneous response to trouble symptoms. Simulators

108

This is a typical Flight Simulator for a large four-engine transport plane. Consoles contain electronic equipment that simulate and record the operations. Trainee sits inside black-covered cockpit in background. *Curtiss-Wright Corp., Electronics Div.*

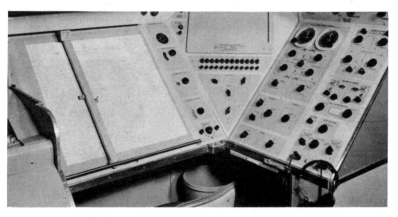

This is the control compartment of the jet plane flight simulator where an instructor is able to set up a number of flying problems which the student must solve. *Link Aviation, Inc.*

can reproduce any type of emergency, thus helping a pilot maintain a ready proficiency in meeting such situations smoothly.

For example, simulators can duplicate the conking out of one or two engines, sudden stalls, fires in the cockpit, and the reversal of propellers at the wrong time. Faced with these make-believe problems, pilots in the simulators practice the necessary corrective measures. All these emergency situations are set up by an instructor stationed at a special control board outside the

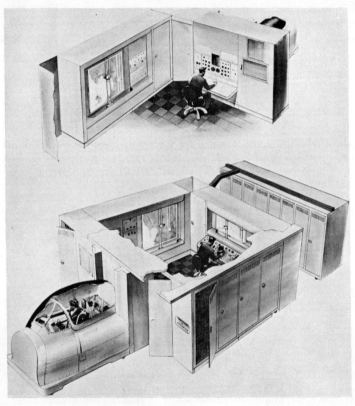

This new U. S. Air Force flight simulator is a 17-ton package of metal, wiring, radar scopes, servo-mechanisms and electronic tubes used to train airmen to fly the F-86D Sabre, an all-weather jet interceptor. The Sabre Flight Simulator has a "built in" enemy plane which the pilot will be required to attack. The simulator requires two instructors, one for flight performance (shown in top view) and the other for radar operations (shown in bottom view). The latter also controls the enemy plane, or target. *North American Aviation, Inc.*

simulator. He can also check on whether the airman is taking the proper measures.

Simulators can be of several different types. The most important, perhaps, is the one which we have just described, which duplicates various flying conditions. Another is the Instrument Trainer. This simulator, whose name is self-explanatory, aids airmen to become familiar with the score or more of instruments that crowd an airplane cockpit. Some of the more important of these are electronic navigation and blind-landing instruments. Usually, if a new instrument is being adapted to an airplane, pilots first become familiar with it in the simulator. Still others, equally specialized, may be for gunnery training or jet operational instructions.

Rescue Devices

Military air operations today, particularly those of the United States, cover vast areas of the world. Many of these require flights over lonely stretches of ocean. When Air Force or Naval fliers are forced to land disabled planes in these regions, it is often difficult to locate survivors either from the air or ships at sea.

In an attempt to overcome the problem there has recently been developed an electronic rescue beacon which downed flyers can use to signal rescuers. The device is known as SARAH—

This is how an airman forced down at sea would call for help with the use of SARAH. *Simmonds Aerocessories, Inc.*

which stands for "search rescue and homing"—and was originally developed in England. It is now being produced in the United States. The rescue beacon is said to be as effective on land as it is on water, for which it was really intended.

SARAH is an extremely light unit, weighing 3¼ pounds, and is supposed to be worn by an airman. It consists of an antenna almost three feet long that is coiled up when not in use. There is also a tiny transmitter which is called the beacon because it sends out radio pulses the way a lighthouse sends out light rays. These signals are not just ordinary pulses, but can be flashed out in groups or varied in such a way as not to interfere with those being transmitted by other downed airmen close by. The beacon signals are flashed outward in a horizontal pattern in all directions and also in a vertical beam. The vertical beacon signal beam is in the shape of an upside-down cone.

When the set is working at full power, its signals can be detected by rescue airplanes at a distance of 66 miles and at an altitude of 10,000 feet. For a surface ship, however, this range is reduced to about 6 miles. The other portion of SARAH equipment, the receiving unit, is carried either aboard an airplane or surface ship. It is made up of three items, a receiver, power pack and an antenna. The heart of the receiver is a small cathode-ray tube which provides a visual record of the incoming distress signals. The screen of the tube is 3″ in diameter and is divided by a vertical line.

An incoming signal flashing on either side of the vertical mark helps give the search plane pilot the correct directional information. The signals usually appear as bright green bars. As long as they maintain the same length, the rescuers know they are heading in the right direction. The signals disappear when the rescue plane enters the vertical cone of distress signals. Once this occurs, the downed airman and the rescuers on the search plane can talk to each other by means of a two-way radio hook-up. This, too, is a part of SARAH's equipment.

The United States Air Force also has another means for

Radio-controlled lifeboat being launched from rescue plane. *Official Air Force Photo.*

rescuing flyers who have been forced down at sea. This one consists of a radio-controlled lifeboat that is flown to the scene of the survivors by a multi-engine rescue plane. The lifeboat, which measures 30' in length, is so constructed that it fits snugly beneath the belly of the rescue aircraft and can be dropped to the water by parachute. The boat is fitted with stabilizing fins at one end which help the parachute keep it upright during the descent. A motor propels the craft through the water, and it carries sufficient fuel for an 800-miles journey. The rescue boat weighs 3,500 pounds and is large enough to hold 15 men. The most important equipment aboard the lifeboat, however, is the electronic robot which permits those on the rescue plane to

The engine of the U. S. Air Force's new radio-controlled lifeboat can be started and operated by an easy push-button switch. *Westinghouse Photo.*

113

control its movements until the survivors are picked up. Those who have perfected the electronic lifeboat say that it has its "brain" on the plane and that it carries a "nervous system" within itself.

Once the rescue boat is in the water, a series of five different radio signals are sent out from the plane telling the craft what to do. The boat's "nervous system," which enables it to carry out orders, consists of a complex system of sensitive detectors, electronic amplifier tubes, relays, and mechanical actuators. The first of the radio signals flashed to the electronic receiver instructs the boat to drop off the stabilizer fins. Another quickly follows that orders the guard to be taken off the rudder and propeller. Still a third directs that air vents be opened in the engine compartment and a blower started to rid the area of possible gas fumes. A fourth signal orders the engine to be

The U. S. Air Force's radio-controlled lifeboat taking orders from its electronic pilot. *Westinghouse Photo.*

choked and cranked as often as necessary until it starts. Finally a fifth radio order directs the electronic "nervous system" to engage the clutch of the motor, move the gear shift from neutral to forward, and advance the throttle to half speed. The boat at this point is now moving through the water to the downed airmen.

The operator aboard the plane is able to guide the lifeboat in the correct direction by a series of other radio impulses which are flashed to a magnetic compass-steering mechanism. A different radio signal is flashed from the remote-control board to turn the boat either to the right or left. The rescue craft, of course, can also be stopped once it reaches the survivors. The airborne lifeboat's control system has been so arranged that once the downed airmen have climbed aboard, they can control the operations of the boat by means of a series of push buttons. These are connected to the vessel's "nervous system" so that the men may start, stop, or steer it at will. During a series of rugged tests, the rescue boat and its remote-control system worked with excellent results. Rescue devices, of course, are just one phase in the application of electronics by the military. There are many others.

Television without Entertainment

Since the advent of practical TV transmission during the years immediately following the end of World War II, a great rush has been under way to adapt it to a wide variety of uses other than that of home entertainment. This technical activity is just as intense among military groups as it is among civilian. One illustration is the Army Signal Corps' recent announcement that they have developed an improved type of TV equipment for use aboard aircraft.

The equipment consists of a TV camera, transmitter and other auxiliary devices. It weighs about 425 pounds and can be easily carried in a single-engine airplane if necessary. In tests with this airborne unit, engineers were able to pick up ground targets 20 miles distant from an altitude of 1,000 feet and transmit them with extreme clearness. Tests have even been made from heights of 3,000 feet with objects 60 miles distant being televised. This is thought to be the maximum range for the set at the moment because picture clarity at that point begins to diminish.

This Army-developed airborne TV equipment is not a

This is a type of television camera tube known as an Image Dissector, used largely for industrial TV systems. Internal parts of tube are shown to left and right. *International Nickel Co.*

pioneer in this field, similar devices having been tried before. But the new unit is said to be a great improvement over the older equipment since it is more reliable, simpler to operate, more compact, and produces clearer pictures. The feeling among military people pressing the development of airborne television equipment is that it can have an important effect on future military operations. Field commanders, for example, provided with TV receivers at their command posts, could be given a continuous pictorial report of the action taking place in their area. Vital decisions might therefore be made with more assurance and a lot faster than by the more conventional methods of aerial photographs or telephone reports. Such airborne TV units are also looked upon as a valuable instrument in peacetime, particularly during periods of great disasters such as floods or uncontrolled forest fires.

Guided Missiles

One of the most startling military technical developments to come out of World War II was that of guided missiles. Although the early pioneering models used were comparatively crude, they nevertheless pointed to a future potential of great wartime effectiveness. Military strategists were greatly impressed with them and during the postwar years tremendous engineering efforts have been conducted to make them even more deadly.

Although guided missiles are the end product of many lines of technical activity, they are dependent perhaps most of all on electronics for their successful operation. Indeed, the two are practically inseparable. It is largely this close association between electronics and missiles which has given birth to a popular expression of our modern language, "push-button warfare." To many people that phrase just about sums up the nature of any future war.

Because missiles roar through the air without any human control, they must have the ability to fly along a precise route and pick out an objective destined for destruction whether in the air or on the earth's surface. Electronics supplies the artificial "brains" which permit these aerial vehicles to carry out their military chores in the most uncanny fashion. There are three major electronic systems employed today for the guidance of missiles. One is called the Command System, another the Beam Rider, and the third the Homing Guidance System.

The Command System requires the least amount of "brain" power on the part of the missile. Essentially the system employs a radar-tracking unit on the ground for guiding the missile through the air, a second radar set for picking up the aerial target to be destroyed and an electronic computer. The ground units find out all the essential information such as speed, height and direction which the missile needs for intercepting the target. This data is relayed to the electronic receiver aboard the missile which directs the latter's controls accordingly in order for it to hit a target. The greater portion of the intelligence in this guidance system is ground-based and subjects the missile to its commands.

117

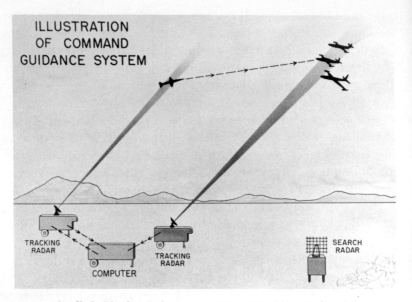

ILLUSTRATION
OF COMMAND
GUIDANCE SYSTEM

TRACKING
RADAR

COMPUTER

TRACKING
RADAR

SEARCH
RADAR

Applied Physics Laboratory, Johns Hopkins University.

Missiles using the Beam Rider system to intercept an aerial target travel along a highway of electromagnetic waves flashed upward by radar. The electronic equipment carried by the aerial weapon is of such a sensitive nature that it responds completely to the influence of these radar radio waves and keeps the missile within the bounds of the beam. The "brain" power of the Beam Rider system is about equally divided between the missile and the ground-based equipment. Missiles guided by radar beams have been developed to the point where they are now extremely accurate in hitting an objective in the sky. These weapons are designed primarily for defense purposes against raiding enemy aircraft.

The United States Army recently unveiled one of the newest in this family of missile weapons, called the "Nike." This missile has a range of about 25 miles and a speed of more than 1,500 miles per hour. Guided by a radar beam, the Nike has shown itself to be almost 100 per cent accurate in hitting aerial targets.

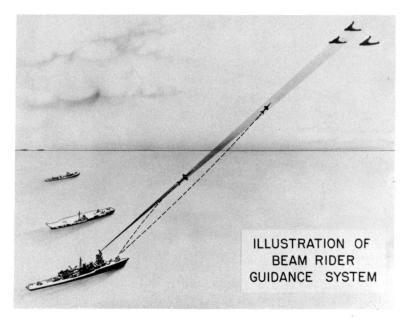

ILLUSTRATION OF
BEAM RIDER
GUIDANCE SYSTEM

Applied Physics Laboratory, Johns Hopkins University.

It is said to be thoroughly capable of coping with any aircraft even of supersonic speeds. A number of defense installations using the Nike are being established at vital points in the United States to keep guard against sudden hostile air attacks.

The third system for directing pilotless air weapons, the Homing method, is one of the most complex of all. The reason for this is that the missile carries all the electronic equipment necessary for flying a selected course, to seek out its victim and to track it down until destroyed. The electronic "brain" in this system is supplemented by radar which helps the missile search for the target. Missiles belonging to this guidance family may be launched either from the ground or from an airplane.

The Homing Guidance includes, among a host of other items, complicated and compact electronic circuits, a computer, a series of small and very sensitive gyroscopes and a number of servo-mechanisms. The last, responding to electronic instruc-

119

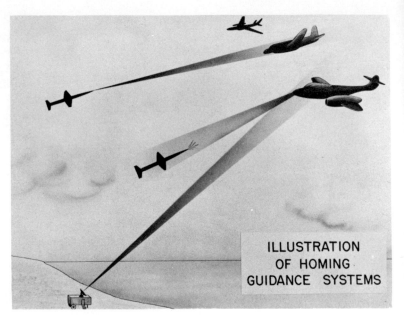

Applied Physics Laboratory, Johns Hopkins University.

tions from the "brain," provides the power needed to move the missile's rudder and ailerons and do other tasks where force is required.

There is also a fourth method of guidance known as the Navigation System. With this the missile must carry its own complete self-contained electronic "brain" that uses the stars or a man-made navigational aid such as Loran to reach its predetermined target. Missiles employing this guidance control are expected to be of the long-range bombardment type.

Anti-Aircraft Control

In line with more conventional anti-aircraft defense weapons, the United States Army has also acquired a newly developed gun that is electronically controlled and almost completely automatic in nature. The weapon is known as the "Skysweeper" and its accuracy is such that it is said to be capable of bringing down

The U. S. Army's newest electronically controlled anti-aircraft gun called the Skysweeper. *U. S. Army Photograph.*

aircraft traveling at near-supersonic speed. The key units connected with the anti-aircraft gun are radar and an electronic computer which is often better known as an "electronic brain."

The radar equipment seeks out sky targets at night and in any kind of bad weather. It collects information such as altitude, speed and direction of the intended victim, then passes it along to the computer. Given the necessary data, the "brain" next takes over the gun's operation. It aims the weapon in the proper direction and tells when to start firing. Incidentally, the radar beam can pick out targets as far distant as 15 miles. Because of the bewildering speed and precision with which the radar and computer operate, the anti-aircraft weapon can be switched automatically, quickly and accurately from one target to another.

The Skysweeper is also equipped with devices that automatically load and ram it. The weapon can fire forty-five 75-mm. shells a minute. It is extremely complex, requiring a crew of eight men to handle it. The Skysweeper is highly mobile and can be set up for full automatic operation in about fifteen minutes. In the event something goes wrong with the complicated electronic controls, this newest of the Army's anti-aircraft weapons can be operated manually.

121

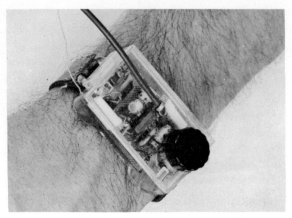

The U. S. Army's "Dick Tracy Wrist Radio" developed by the Signal Corps' Engineering Laboratories. *U. S. Army Signal Corps.*

The Wrist-Radio

While hardly on the same level of importance as some of the military electronic developments just described, the announcement by the Army Signal Corps of a new wrist radio is certainly fascinating. Known as the "Dick Tracy," after the famous comic strip detective who forecast the use of such a device, the midget radio receiver was created mostly as an experiment in miniaturization. This last is one of the latest technical developments in electronics. Although its military value at the moment is strictly limited, the picture may change after further improvement.

The peanut-size wrist radio is 2" long, 1⅛" wide, and 3" thick. It weighs 2⅝ ounces and is enclosed within a plexiglass case. Instead of conventional electronic tubes, the midget radio is equipped with transistors—the latest means of generating electronic energy. The various parts of the set are connected by still another of electronics' latest developments, the printed circuit. The wiring in the chassis is accomplished by an etching process. We will discuss both these electronic advances in more detail further on.

Because transistors require so little power to operate, the designers of the midget radio were able to use a tiny mercury battery no bigger than the tip of a pencil. The Dick Tracy is also equipped with an antenna and an earpiece that looks very much like a hearing aid. The wires for both these items are hidden under the sleeve of the wearer. There is also an off-and-on switch fixed to the radio as well as a tuning knob so that various stations can be selected. In tests so far, this tiny radio has been able to pick up stations as far distant as forty miles. It does not transmit.

Reading Weather Conditions

Weather conditions are an important factor in any type of military operation. This has always been so and will undoubtedly be true in any future conflicts. For this reason military forces the world over have placed a great deal of emphasis on the development of a large variety of apparatus for predicting weather conditions as accurately as possible. One of the latest produced for the use of United States military forces is called RAWIN, a name derived from the words radio-wind.

RAWIN is an automatic wind recording system that eliminates an older one requiring hand operation. The equipment consists of a mobile automatic tracking radio direction finder and an improved type of radiosonde, a midget radio set that records and transmits weather data as it is borne skyward by a gas-filled balloon. Rising higher and higher, the radiosonde picks up and sends back to the ground automatically such information as wind speed, wind direction, barometric pressure, temperature, and humidity. Among other things the midget airborne weather station is equipped with a hygrometer for humidity readings, a barometer for measuring air pressure, a transmitter for sending this data back to earth and a miniature battery to provide power for the transmitter. The unit weighs close to two pounds and in size is comparable to a telephone.

To receive the radio information sent out by the airborne weather station, it is vitally important for ground-based equip-

This is the U. S. Army's new RAW-IN or ground meteorological direction finder about to keep track of a weather balloon. *U. S. Army Photograph.*

A newly developed facsimile device shown transmitting a weather map. *Muirhead & Co., Ltd.*

ment to keep the radiosonde constantly in view. This is the job of RAWIN's newly improved automatic tracking radio direction finder. The apparatus can keep a radiosonde in view no matter what altitude it may climb to. Formerly the limit of the tracking device was about 100,000 feet. The direction finder has a bowl-shaped antenna assembly that concentrates the radio waves flashed earthward by the midget weather station. This weather-finding equipment can easily be taken into the field on a two-wheel trailer or, if necessary, it may be broken down into smaller units and carried by troops themselves.

The Telephone

Ever since the time Fleming created his "valve" for the detection of wireless signals, electronics has been of particular importance to the field of communication. Throughout the first half of this century, as scientists learned more about the behavior of electrons and developed better ways to control and put them to work, communications always seemed to reap the first benefits of each new achievement. And this applies perhaps most of all to the telephone.

During the first decade of this century telephone communication was still in its youth, limited in the distance across which one person could talk to another. When the telephone was first invented, in 1876, its range was restricted to the confines of a single building, later expanding to cover a city-wide area. After about ten years its scope had gradually broadened to intercity communication, the longest line at that time stretching from New York to Boston. By the turn of the century the human voice could be transmitted only as far as Chicago. Then Dr. Lee De Forest created his famous audion vacuum tube and an entirely new world opened up for telephone communications.

Adapting the principles of De Forest's electron tube for their own special purposes, telephone engineers by 1915 had vacuum amplifier tubes of such power that they could easily boost the weak signals of the human voice for transmission across the

United States. Again employing their new powerful electron tubes, telephone engineers in that same year established an historic radio-telephone link between Arlington, Virginia, and the Eiffel Tower in Paris, France. They followed this up in quick succession with other connections to the Hawaiian Islands and the Panama Canal Zone. But the transoceanic telephone link was only experimental and a good many years elapsed involving painstaking development before it could be put on a permanent basis. Not until 1927 did telephone engineers establish regular telephone service between the United States and England.

Thanks to technical advances in electronics, particularly in improving amplifying and detecting tubes, the overseas service has expanded enormously since that historic year. Now it is possible for a person in the United States to talk to another in almost 100 foreign countries.

Perhaps nowhere else in the world has the telephone become so intimate a part of everyone's social and business life as in the United States. A veritable spider-web of telephone connections are spread over this country, serving 75,000 cities and towns and more than 2,000,000 farms. Keeping pace with the expanded telephone services, or perhaps one should say, promoting the spread of telephone usage, has been the steady progress in technical improvements. While a good deal of research has concentrated on better vacuum tubes, these have been by no means the only elements involved. Dozens of other electronic items such as relays, condensers, and resistors have also played a part in the continuous improvement in telephone communications.

The telephone network that interlocks every city and hamlet in the United States is an enormously complex structure. This is an outright result of the huge demands for the service. At the moment there are something like 49,000,000 telephones in use in the United States. The use of these telephones makes possible a total number of connections amounting to the staggering figure of 1,200,000,000,000,000! Of course nothing near this sum does take place, but it has been estimated that more than 200,000,000 calls are made daily in the United States, which is an impressive figure. The point is that handling such a volume of calls taxes human abilities to the utmost in providing swift, dependable service. Therefore automatic electronic-mechanical devices and arrangements have been created to help out. The best known of these, of course, is the dial system.

Almost everyone is familiar with this method of placing a call, in which the dialed number sends electrical impulses racing to complicated electronic-mechanical equipment in a central office where the connection is made automatically and with bewildering speed. The human operator in a sense has been replaced with an electronic robot. At first dial systems were confined to local areas, then spread gradually to encompass entire cities and nearby towns. Now telephone engineers are hastening the day when this automatic connecting system will be commonplace for calls placed throughout the nation. A milestone towards that objective was passed in the summer of 1953 when engineers of the New Jersey Bell Telephone took the wraps off an electronic giant called a Translator. This unit has begun to reduce by almost half the time normally required for nationwide phone calls.

The Translator is a bewildering array of wires, lenses, mirrors, powerful light beams, tiny electronic cells called photo-transistors that are electrically sensitive to light and a collection of metal cards each punched with a distinctive series of holes. Once all this is activated by electrical impulses, the Translator automatically first picks out the most direct and quickest route to the distant city for which the call is intended. If this particular circuit is blocked off, the electronic "brain" will find an alternate route all within a split second. The Translator has made necessary a minor change in the normal process of dialing a number. A three-digit code number has been added to the regular number being dialed. The code numbers represent 99 areas throughout the United States and Southern Canada.

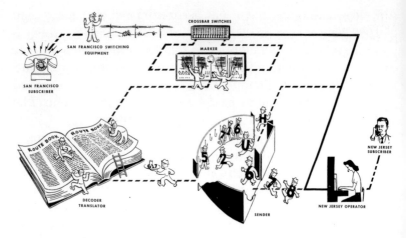

A general idea how Newark 4A dialing equipment, of which the Translator is the heart, works. When the operator dials, the signals are stored in the Sender apparatus, which signals a Decoder-Translator to study the instructions and find out what route to take. The Marker is asked to test to see if a circuit to San Francisco is available. Finding one, the Marker joins it to the line over which the operator dialed. Then the Crossbar Switches take over. The Sender, Decoder-Translator and Marker bow out, their work done in one second or less, and are ready for another call. *New Jersey Bell Telephone.*

Batteries of relay switches, 130,000 of them, used by the Translator. *New Jersey Bell Telephone.*

When a call is placed to some distant city, the code number is always first selected as representing the area in which the exchange is located.

If a telephone call is placed, let us say, to someone in Boston, the operator will receive the number and immediately begin to press keys on her switchboard representing the number desired. The operator is actually relaying the message to the electronic robot. The Translator now goes into action. First one of its metal cards, containing a code that conforms to the number being called, drops into the path of the rays of light. All the light is blocked off by the card except that which passes through the pattern of a certain few holes. These needle-thin streams of light pass to the far end of the apparatus and fall upon several of the photo-transistors. These tiny electronic cells react electrically to the light rays and flash impulses over dozens of wires to groups of small switches called relays.

The relays are arranged in such manner that they start and control a search throughout the vast network of circuits at the central office for the best route to Boston. In less than one second this job is done, and in addition a substitute circuit has been selected in case the first is not available. According to the engineers who developed this long-distance automatic dialing apparatus, fifteen to thirty seconds is a fair average from the moment when the operator begins pushing keys until the bell rings at the receiving end.

The Translator and all its attendant equipment, many portions of which weigh from a half-ton to a ton, required four years to develop and cost $15,000,000. It occupies three floors in the New Jersey Bell Telephone Company's Newark exchange. This automatic long-distance dialing system is also known as Newark 4-A. It required more than 22,000 miles of wire to link up the various elements in the system, which contains something like 130,000 relay switches. All of this illustrates the complexity of just one little segment of a nationwide telephone system.

Two-Way Mobile Telephone

Telephone communications are not limited to the types we have discussed so far. In recent years, again as electronic devices became more effective, other forms began to develop such as two-way mobile telephone hook-ups. Unlike conventional telephone systems, the two-way radio-telephone depends for the most part on transmitting and receiving without the aid of

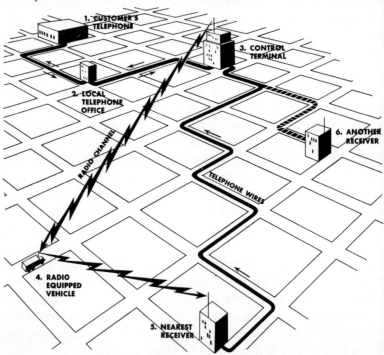

The customer (1) asks to be connected with mobile service. His call goes through the local telephone office (2) and on to the control terminal (3) where a special operator signals the vehicle he wants (4) by radio. The driver answers, his voice traveling by radio to the nearest receiver (5), thence by telephone wires, via the control terminal (3) and the local telephone office (2) to the customer's telephone (1). If the vehicle had been in the vicinity of another receiver (6) when called, the driver's answer would have traveled through the dotted telephone line to the control terminal (3). *A. T. & T. Co.*

wires. Electromagnetic waves confined to a specific frequency are the normal carriers of messages.

Typical equipment of this kind may include a radio transmitter, a radio receiver, a control unit with hand set and a power source. The control unit may have a switch for turning the power "on" or "off," signals which light up to show when the power is "on," a bell that rings when an incoming call arrives and finally a hand telephone which fits into a hanger beneath the unit. The handset contains a button switch which must be pressed down in order for the user to talk and be released for listening. Calls coming into a vehicle with this two-way radio-telephone equipment are first sent to a control terminal where a special operator signals the vehicle by radio. When contact is established, the person receiving the call has his responses flashed by radio waves to the nearest receiving station in his area. From this point his message travels along conventional telephone wires via the original control terminal to the phone of the individual who first placed the call.

Two-way radio-telephone systems have been developed in a variety of forms for a number of communication purposes. Transcontinental buses have them so drivers may make periodic reports to their dispatch offices. In return, they may also receive the very latest travel orders. Newspapers have equipped many of the cars used by their reporters so the latter can send details of incidents directly from the scene into the editorial offices.

Two-way radio telephone employed by an ambulance driver. *A. T. & T. Co.*

131

Police cars and fire-fighting vehicles have long made use of two-way radio-telephone equipment which has helped enormously in the handling of emergencies. Craft such as tugboats, ferries, fireboats, fishing boats, and pleasure yachts also find this magic electronics communication system an asset in their activities. Railroads are among the latest to benefit from the use of radio-telephone hook-ups, adding one more type of communication to the variety which they already employ.

Railroads have long been interested in a communications arrangement whereby messages could be sent from one portion of a train to another or from a fixed point to a moving train and vice versa. Years of experimental work along this line met with repeated failure until the years immediately after World War II, when technical progress in electronics easily solved the problem. Typical of the radio-telephone systems employed by railroads is that developed by the Erie, one of the first to adapt this type of communication for its specialized activities.

The mobile equipment is usually set up in the cab of the train's engine. It includes a handset which the engineer and fireman both can use for sending messages and a loudspeaker fixed to the wall of the cab. This last item permits the crew to hear all calls taking place within range of the apparatus. The antenna needed for transmission is attached to the roof of the cab. The power source for operating the radio-telephone hook-up, which incidentally uses very high frequencies among electromagnetic waves, is housed in the nose of the engine.

If the train is a freight, similar equipment is placed in the caboose. In this case, the power source is placed under the floor of the caboose and includes a storage battery and an axle-driven generator. The radio-telephone system developed and used by the Erie Railroad has also been installed in many of their wayside stations along their train routes so that it has great versatility in usage.

The radio-telephone also permits the crews of a train to communicate with other railroad personnel at the wayside stations.

132

Portable radio unit like this helps to expedite railroad yard operations. *New York Central System.*

This allows an exchange of orders or other information between the two units. A train crew may also speak with the crew of another train within the maximum range of their equipment. This is helpful because the crew of one train may see something wrong on the passing cars of another, such as swinging doors or shifted freight, and thus warn the unsuspecting trainmen about it. Finally, operators at wayside stations utilize the two-way radio-telephone hook-up to communicate with each other and with a central dispatch point. The radio-telephone arrangement serves as an important link in the railroad's overall communication system. This is especially valuable in times of emergency when, through natural or other causes, certain portions of the system may break down.

Microwaves for Communications

One of the newest and most fascinating of the electronic developments in the field of communications is the use of microwaves for transmission purposes. Long before World War II, when scientists were experimenting with electromagnetic waves for radar, it occurred to many that certain of these very same waves could be used for flashing messages through the air. In the spring of 1931 an event occurred which bore out this theory. At that time groups of government officials and scientists as-

Control panel connected to remote radar installation in railroad yard. Speedmeter recorders at left show car speeds as they enter group retarders. *Southern Railway System.*

sembled on the cliffs of Dover and Calais to witness the first microwave demonstration for transmitting messages. Although the wavelengths of electromagnetic radiations used for this historic experiment were far longer than those now employed, about 7″ in length, the principles of the system with its parabolic reflectors is still essentially the same.

Scientists and engineers involved with communications problems were impressed with the microwave demonstration and carried on the work of improving it. Three years later, in 1934, the world witnessed the first microwave transmission line when the English airport of Lympne and St. Inglevert, France, were connected. These two points were separated by about 35 miles. Gradually thereafter microwave wave links were established in various other parts of Europe. But these early microwave systems were far from the efficient hook-ups which exist today. They were able to handle only one or two channels of signals because of the limitations of the type of wavelengths which could be produced at the time.

Scientists knew that the higher the frequencies, and therefore the shorter the electromagnetic waves possible, the more signals or channels microwave beams could carry. The usefulness of microwave transmission would therefore increase enormously. It was the tremendous surge of technical advances in electronics, particularly in newer and more powerful tubes, during World War II and the immediate postwar years, that finally made the higher frequencies available in the microwave region. As a result, microwave transmission is growing by leaps and bounds into one of the most important chains in the communication systems that link our world together.

Microwaves, similar to light waves, travel in a straight line. They do not bend around the earth's curve and therefore, in order to prevent them from disappearing out into space, they are beamed from one relay tower to another when used for transmission purposes. A microwave relay beam is of a super-high frequency, vibrating something like four billion times a second. Each electromagnetic wave in the beam is almost the length of a man's little finger. They are invisible, of course, and as an example of their tremendous ability and versatility, a single radio-relay channel of a microwave beam can carry hundreds of telephone messages at the same time or, as they are now commonly called on to do, a television program.

In operation, a microwave radio-relay system works in this fashion. When a telephone call is placed at one end of a coast-to-coast hook-up, let us say, the message starts out in a normal way by wire or cable to a microwave relay tower. Here a powerful transmitter changes the incoming electrical signals into microwaves. The waves are directed to the top of the tower where antenna reflectors, usually bowl-shaped affairs, focus the waves into a narrow beam and flash them through the air to the next relay tower. The towers are usually spaced about 25 or 30 miles apart depending upon their location. They are normally placed on the highest point of a surrounding area. This permits the towers to be separated at the maximum distance.

135

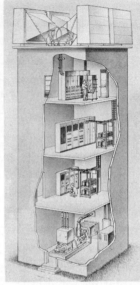

(left) This concrete tower is another type of micro-wave relay station.

(right) This schematic drawing shows the interior arrangement of a typical micro-wave relay station. *A. T. & T. Co.*

Each tower is equipped with a set of sending antennas and receiving antennas. They are both alike in form. When the beam strikes the receiving antenna, the electrical impulses travel to a powerful amplifying unit where they are given a ten-millionfold increase in strength so that they may complete the next portion of their transcontinental journey. After its "booster" shot, the voice-carrying signals, again in the form of a microwave beam, are sent up to the transmitting antenna and flashed through the sky to the next tower. The telephone message follows this procedure more than 100 times until its destination at the other end of the line is reached.

When the electrical impulses reach the final relay tower, they are changed again from microwaves into voice signals and sent along by wire to a very complex electronic receiving unit. Here a particular single call is separated from the hundreds of others that travel the same route and is flashed along wires to the person for whom intended. Although the example just described was for the transmission of a telephone message, the same method holds true for sending television programs across the nation. The only major difference in the latter process is that the microwave beam carries the sound signals as well as the video impulses.

One of the longest microwave radio-relay systems in the United States was established by the Bell Telephone System not long after the end of World War II when the east and west coasts were linked. It supplemented two previously established means of communication within this country, namely, the use of wire strung from pole to pole and the coaxial cable. The latter is also a comparatively recent development and consists primarily of a number of wires bound together into a series of cables which in turn form a large main cable. This transmission line is buried in the ground and can carry multiple telephone messages as well as television signals. Microwave transmission, however, is proving itself far superior to other methods in communications. In comparison with wire-line transmission, it is cheaper to maintain and does not suffer as much from storms or other disasters. Weather disturbances that knock down wires cannot harm invisible microwave beams but actually improve the quality of their transmission.

Microwaves enjoy still another advantage, their great versatility. They can transmit messages by voice, teletype, or even facsimile. By using TV-type signals, microwaves can flash drawings, charts or other kinds of pictures from one point to another. Particularly important is their ability to send electrical impulses through the air with the speed of light for remote control of certain kinds of industrial operations. This last accomplishment is broadening the usefulness of microwaves far beyond its original application in the public communications field.

Electric power, oil and gas companies whose high tension wires and pipelines range over the countryside for many, many miles, are using microwave relay systems for communication purposes and to watch over and operate certain of their far-

These giant parabolic antennas form a vital link in the micro-wave system used to operate the vast power network of the Bonneville Power Administration. They transmit and receive high-frequency radio beams to provide instant voice, telemetering, relaying and video fault-location facilities. *I. T. & T.*

flung installations. Since many functions such as pressure and temperature readings and engine speeds can be converted into electrical impulses, microwaves are being used to transmit this information from outlying installations where there are no workmen in attendance to central stations. Here trained observers study the information that is received and then, again by microwave relay, send out orders to the far-removed equipment which may be started, stopped or regulated. A radio signal is enough to activate certain electrical or mechanical devices to do that job.

One of the most ambitious applications of microwaves in this respect is being carried out in Vancouver, British Columbia. A hydro-electric plant in this area is being operated by remote controls from a central station 72 miles away.

A mid-west oil company uses a micro-wave radio relay system to connect its far-flung facilities. *I. T. & T.*

Electronics in Communications

Electronics has also left its mark on other and older systems of communications such as the telegraph, teletype, wirephoto and even the conventional long-wave radio. Much of the equipment in telegraphy has been converted to an automatic basis for speeding up both the transmission and reception of messages. One device, for example, called the Desk Fax, based on facsimile or radiophoto principles, allows the user to transmit or receive messages instantaneously without the need of messenger pick-up or delivery. A business man who might have a unit of this kind first sends his message to the nearest telegraph office. A Desk Fax at this point receives it and immediately relays it to the person for whom intended. This individual must also be equipped with a Desk Fax in order to receive the message.

Radiophoto systems which instantly transmit photos, charts, maps, finger prints and many other forms of illustrative matter from one point to another, have had the quality and speed of their service improved greatly by electronics. The transmission of pictorial material by means of radio waves was first developed

139

and demonstrated by Alexander Bain of Great Britain in 1842. Since then the methods have undergone many improvements, although the basic principles of the system originated by Bain are still employed.

Essentially, modern equipment calls for a photo or other illustrated matter being transmitted to be scanned over its entire area by an optical device. Light from a scanning beam striking one area of the picture at a time is reflected and picked up by a sensitive photoelectric tube. The tube translates this into electrical impulses equal in strength to the intensity of the light. The light intensity is varied by the different shadings of the picture. The picture is fastened to a drum and is turned at a precise speed and in such a manner that its entire surface is scanned by the light beam.

The receiving unit can be of several types, but the one most frequently used is based on photographic methods. With this, the incoming electric signals carrying the picture control the intensity of a beam of light falling on sensitized paper, which is also wrapped around a drum. The drum is synchronized in speed with the one at the transmitting end so that the same tonal shadings fall in the same areas. Another method uses a stylus which traces the message received on paper treated with a special chemical. Newspapers are frequent users of radiophoto transmission, sending and receiving photos of news events over long distances with great speed. Law enforcement agencies are others who find this communication method valuable for flashing photos and fingerprints of criminals across the country. Airlines rely heavily on this technique for receiving up-to-the-minute weather maps from a central meteorological office.

Radio transmission using long-waves of electrical radiation, the pioneer in this form of communication, has also benefited from discoveries and developments in electronics. The quality, strength of its signals, and range have all been vastly improved. Incidentally, it is interesting to note the nature of long-waves in comparison to microwaves. Long-waves used by broadcasting stations and for transmitting messages over extremely great distances are measured in hundreds of feet rather than inches. Some can be as much as 600 feet from crest to crest. The frequency at which they are flashed through the air is much lower than that for the very short waves. This is gauged in millions of cycles instead of billions.

Top view shows how long radio waves travel. They strike the ionosphere and bounce back to earth. Lower view depicts how microwaves move in straight line out through space. These waves can be cut off by mountains and high buildings. *Allen B. Du Mont Laboratories, Inc.*

Long-waves do not travel in a straight beam-like manner, but are able to make their way around obstacles such as hills and buildings. Microwaves are absorbed by obstructions. At night and frequently during daylight hours, long-waves are bounced back to earth by an ionized layer of air about 150 miles high. It is this electrical reflecting shield, the ionosphere, that permits these waves to travel over long distances. The world's most powerful sending station, the Jim Creek radio transmitter, placed in operation by the United States Navy in the fall of 1953, can send its signals completely around the globe.

The Jim Creek transmitter, at this moment represents the

Big Jim transmitter building nestling in valley between 3,000-foot mountains. One hundred and fifty thousand feet of steel copperweld cable, looped in giant strands across Jim Creek Valley, form the largest radio antenna ever constructed. *Official U. S. Navy Photo.*

peak achievement of scientists and engineers in this form of radio communication. Its power is rated at 1,200,000 watts, which is 22 times greater than the strongest commercial broadcasting station in the United States with its maximum output of 50,000 watts. Four newly developed superpower beam triode electron tubes are responsible for the station's tremendous signal strength. The tubes are protected from sudden overload conditions by an electronic device that goes into action at the incredible speed of seven-millionths of a second.

This powerful Naval transmitter is located in the Cascade Mountains of the State of Washington and from its lofty perch can send messages to any portion of the world, through magnetic storms, ionospheric disturbances and even to submarines

Operators inside the U. S. Navy's "Big Jim" radio transmitter, said to be the most powerful in the world. *Official U. S. Navy Photo.*

under water. Everything about a radio transmitter with such tremendous abilities must be of record-breaking proportions and not the least of these with Jim Creek is the antenna system, the largest ever constructed. The antenna literally forms a "roof" over Jim Creek Valley and the transmitter site. Six 200-foot towers on a 3,200-foot mountaintop north of the transmitter and six others on a 3,000-foot mountain top to the south support the antenna network. Between the towers and across the valley ten spans of the antenna are strung, ranging in length from 5,640 feet to 8,800 feet.

Because of the powerful electromagnetic field which is created around the transmitter area, a grounding mat consisting of more than 200 miles of copper wire is buried in the ground of the valley floor. A huge amount of electric power is needed to operate the world's most powerful transmitter, which averages about 2,000 kilowatts. Engineers have estimated that the transmitter uses enough current daily to operate the average home for a period of one year.

Television

Of all the wonderful communication systems that rely heavily on electronics for their wizard-like performance, none, perhaps, can equal the magic of television. This wondrous instrument which can pluck sound and pictures out of the sky and bring them into our homes, has made us all more acutely aware of the seemingless endless magic of electronics than any other single development in that field.

143

The Camera Tube. Here is one type of camera tube used in the studio where the program is produced. This type is called the image orthicon. The picture is focused by a lens (A) so it throws an image on a photo-sensitive surface (B), much as an ordinary camera focuses an image on a light sensitive film.

Light causes this plate to throw off electrons—many electrons, where the light is bright; few, where dull—and these electrons fly to the nearest point on the target plate (C), which is, of course, the point directly opposite. As each electron strikes the target plate, it knocks loose secondary electrons which are drawn to the wire-mesh screen (D), and carried away.

Loss of these negative electrons, leaves a positive charge on the opposite side of the target plate (C).

In this way, the back of the target plate carries a pattern of electrical charges which always corresponds to the picture—strongly positive where the picture is bright; less positive in the shadows.

The cathode (E), in the opposite end of the tube, sends out an electronic beam (F) which "reads" this electrical pattern just as your eye is reading this page.

As the beam passes along each line, the electron-hungry positive spots snatch electrons out of the beam to replace those that were knocked out.

The beam is reflected (G) with many of its electrons missing. It is no longer of uniform strength. It varies from strong to weak. And in the pattern of its strength is a signal which can be sent out all over the country to millions of receiving sets—information which the receivers reconvert to a picture. *Allen B. Du Mont Laboratories, Inc.*

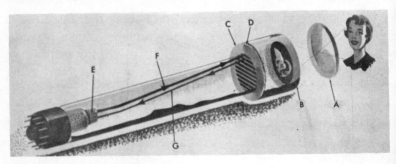

The Picture Tube. Here is the picture tube in the receiving set. The signal from the camera tube, after being received on an antenna and amplified, passes to the grid (B) where it regulates the flow of the electron beam coming from the cathode (A). A magnetic field (C) focuses the beam much as a lens focuses a beam of light. The electron beam is then speeded up by an accelerator (D) before passing thru the magnetic coils (E) which guide the beam from side to side, up and down.

At the screen end of the tube, a high positive voltage applied to a conductor coating on the inside of the tube through connection (F) offers a powerful attraction to the flying electrons so they strike the screen face (G) with great force.

This electron beam, and all the other millions of beams all over the country, must move in exact time with the beam in the camera tube.

To keep them exactly synchronized, a special timing signal is sent out during the brief interval while the beam is jumping back to start another line.

Of course, the electronic beam lights up only one tiny spot on the screen (D) at a time, but it takes the beam only a thirtieth of a second to cover the screen completely and get back to that same spot again, so your eye sees it as a complete picture. *Allen B. Du Mont Laboratories, Inc.*

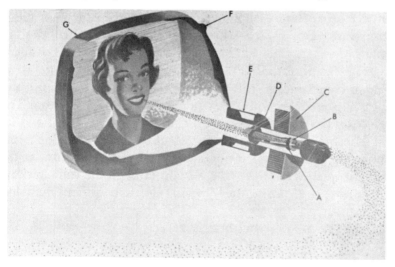

The magic of television is made possible mainly through the cathode-ray tube, one form of which is located in the TV camera and the other in the receiving set. There are several types of camera tubes employed to pick up a scene for television purposes. One is known as the Image Dissector, while another, the most commonly used, is called the Image Orthicon. Television transmission and reception operates essentially in this manner. For our purpose we will assume the orthicon tube is doing the televising.

The scene being televised is focused by a lens at the front of the tube and made to fall on a photo-sensitive mosaic plate. This is a short distance behind the lens, corresponding to a light-sensitive film in an ordinary camera. The mosaic plate is made of a flat piece of mica and covered with millions of silver particles. Each of these particles is coated with cesium oxide, making it sensitive to light.

Directly back of the mosaic plate is fixed a second surface called a conducting plate which transforms each of the silver particles into a tiny capacitor. The capacitors, influenced by the focused varying light intensity of the image, are the source of the released electrons. The millions of tiny capacitors have now become positive, or electron-releasing, in varying degrees, in direct proportion to the amount of light focused upon them. They are more positive where the light is bright and less so in the darker areas, emitting many or few electrons respectively.

The electrons are picked up by a collector ring that carries a positive charge. At this point the cathode at the opposite end of the tube comes into play, sending out an electron beam. The electron beam scans the mosaic plate from left to right and up and down with incredible speed. As the beam moves along each line, the millions of tiny positively-charged capacitors on the mosaic steal electrons from the beam through the common conducting plate. Thus they regain electrons which they lost previously.

The electron beam then is reflected to the cathode, but

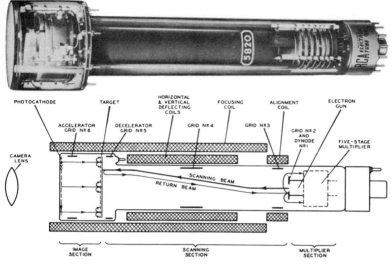

Structure of RCA–5820 Image Orthicon. This tube type is used in broadcast television cameras for both studio and outdoor pickup. *Radio Corporation of America.*

changed in nature. Its strength is no longer uniform, but instead it carries a voltage variation corresponding exactly to the variation of the electrical charges on the light-sensitive capacitors. This varying voltage, an electronic equivalent of the image being televised, is then amplified and sent coursing through an antenna and flashed through the air to be picked up by countless numbers of television receivers.

At the receiving end of the television transmission, the signals are picked up by an antenna, amplified in a receiving set and then passed along to the grid in the picture tube. The latter is also basically a cathode tube whose electron beam flow is regulated by the grid. That part of the picture tube which shoots out the electron beam is called an electron gun. It is equipped with an electrostatic field, a device that fits like a ring around a portion of the gun. This electrostatic field operates automatically, and its job is to focus the beam of electrons just as a lens would focus a ray of light.

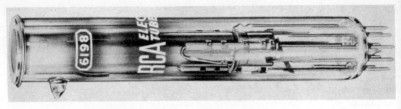

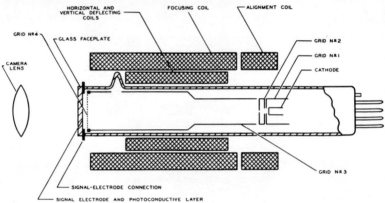

Structure of RCA–6198 Vidicon. This tube is designed for use in television cameras, primarily in industrial service. *Radio Corporation of America.*

There is another grid device, called an accelerator, that also affects the electron beam. It speeds up the velocity of the stream of electrons as they flash out of the gun. After the accelerator acts upon the beam of electrons, the latter influenced by a magnetic field produced by coils of magnets fixed around the neck of the tube. This magnetic control guides the beam up and down and from side to side as it strikes the inner side of the tube's face.

The inside portion of the picture tube at the screen end is coated with an electron-sensitive substance and then electrified with a very high voltage. This electric field aids the madly onrushing beam of electrons to increase its speed so that it strikes the viewing screen with tremendous force. The electron beam carrying the picture signals is synchronized in motion with the one in the camera tube so that the same areas of the scene

148

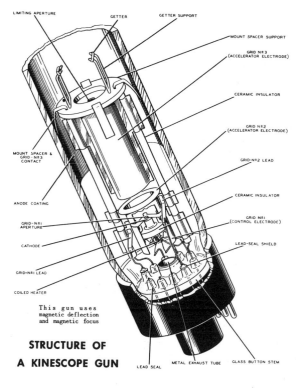

LIMITING APERTURE
GETTER
GETTER SUPPORT
MOUNT SPACER SUPPORT
GRID N°3 (ACCELERATOR ELECTRODE)
CERAMIC INSULATOR
GRID N°2 (ACCELERATOR ELECTRODE)
GRID-N°2 LEAD
CERAMIC INSULATOR
GRID N°I (CONTROL ELECTRODE)
MOUNT SPACER & GRID-N°3 CONTACT
LEAD-SEAL SHIELD
ANODE COATING
GRID-N°I APERTURE
CATHODE
GRID-N°I LEAD
COILED HEATER
LEAD SEAL
METAL EXHAUST TUBE
GLASS BUTTON STEM

This gun uses magnetic deflection and magnetic focus

STRUCTURE OF A KINESCOPE GUN

This gun uses magnetic deflection and magnetic focus. *Radio Corporation of America.*

being televised are reproduced simultaneously. The picture pattern it traces on the tube's inner surface is exactly the same in gradations of light and darkness as that picked up by the camera tube.

The electron beam in the receiving tube covers the viewing screen with the same number of lines of light and dark variations as that scanned by the camera tube. During the split second that the beam has finished one trace line and hops back to begin another, a special timing signal is sent out by the transmitter which helps to control the synchronization of the transmitting and receiving electron beams. The picture-carrying electron beam lights up, one speck at a time, the phosphor-

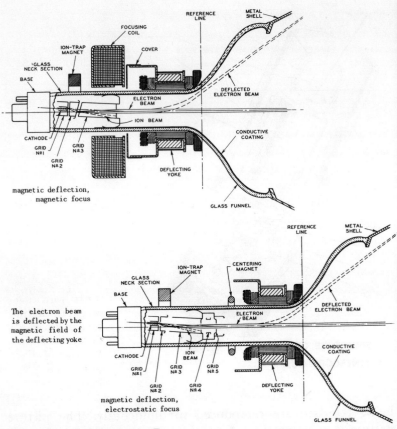

The electron beam is deflected by the magnetic field of the deflecting yoke

magnetic deflection, magnetic focus

magnetic deflection, electrostatic focus

Structure of Kinescopes. *Radio Corporation of America.*

coated inner face of the tube as it flashes across the entire area. It moves with such amazing speed that the entire screen is covered in one-thirtieth of a second before the beam returns to its original point. The light and dark lines make up the picture we see on the face of the tube.

From the very outset of its introduction to the public, television captured the interest and imagination of people everywhere with its ability to bring the world of entertainment, public events and education right into one's home. At first its range

A mobile television transmitting unit used by the Du Mont television network. *Allen B. Du Mont Laboratories, Inc.*

was limited to within a hundred miles of a transmitting station because of the nature of the electromagnetic waves used to carry TV signals. Since these are in the microwave family, they travel in a straight line and then disappear into space. They do not curve with the earth's surface and therefore have limited range. But this problem was soon overcome with microwave relay stations and the coaxial cable, so that today in the United States, for example, there is scarcely a section of the country not covered by TV signals. At the moment of this writing, there exist throughout the United States more than three hundred television transmitters, with more being added monthly. Millions of homes are equipped with one or more TV receivers.

Keeping pace with its purely physical growth is the electronic research of scientists and engineers who are endeavoring to advance the art of television to still greater heights of achievement. In the short period of television's practical existence we have already seen the fruits of their labors in improved transmission and larger and clearer picture tubes. Now they are striving to place television on a world-wide basis within the very near future. Of more immediate concern, however, they have succeeded in adding color to TV transmission, a feature which promises a great increase in the value of this medium.

Color Television

Color television is basically the same as black-and-white except for the addition of those elements needed to convert a colored spectrum into electronic impulses and back again into a colored image. Several ways have been developed by which

Some of the controls inside Du Mont's mobile TV transmitter. *Allen B. Du Mont Laboratories, Inc.*

colored images can be transmitted and received. But the system approved by the Federal Communications Commission to inaugurate color television in the United States is the compatible method because signals can be televised and received in both color and black-and-white. The system was largely produced under the guidance of the National Television System Committee, a group of engineers representing the television industry. The main advantage of the compatible method as compared to others is that TV sets in current use do not become obsolete if certain programs are transmitted exclusively in color.

Within the compatible method itself we find several different ways of televising in color. One of these utilizes a camera having three color pick-up tubes. Each tube is responsible for a single primary color, red, green, or blue (not to be confused with the primary colors used in the field of art). The scene being televised is first viewed through the camera lens and then directed to an arrangement of mirrors. These are called dichroic mirrors and they have the special quality of separating a scene into individual bands of color. Thus the televised scene is separated into three colored images—red, green, and blue. The mirrors reflect these three images back to the camera tubes, which respond only to the particular hue received.

Before reaching their objective, however, the images first travel through another lens and a correction filter. Each filter allows only the proper color value to pass on to an individual camera tube. The camera tubes then convert the images into electrical signals representing the three primary colors. These color-carrying signals move along two different paths. One group of the three individual signals goes to a unit called an "adder." This electronic device mixes up the color signals in the correct proportion and then transforms them into a black and white signal. Meanwhile the second group of primary color signals travels to another electronic unit known as an "encoder." Its job is to combine all three impulses into one signal having color and color intensity. The two TV signals resulting from the passage through the "adder" and "encoder"—one carrying the black-and-white information and the other the color—are then sent flashing through the air together by the transmitter.

If the two signals are picked up by a television receiver designed only for monochrome reception, then the black-and-white signal is used exclusively. A color receiver, however, welcomes the two signals which pass on to a color "separator" inside the set. Here the two traveling electrical partners are

A color television camera in action. *Radio Corporation of America.*

separated. The color signal moves along into a "decoder" where it is transformed back into three individual color signals. The black-and-white signal is then combined with these to give them the proper amount of brightness.

The picture tube handling the incoming color signals contains three electron guns instead of one as in the black-and-white receiver. The electron beam that shoots out of each gun is influenced by one of the three primary color signals, red, green or blue. The timing and intensity of these colored electron beams is affected by the incoming signals. As the beams leave their respective guns, they are made to converge at a single point on a masking plate which is located a short distance in back of the viewing screen.

The masking plate is perforated with a number of tiny holes which serve as passageways for the tricolor beams as they sweep vertically and horizontally across the face of the plate. Magnetic coils, like those in a black-and-white tube, guide the swift movements of the beams up and down and from side to side. The incoming signals control the three beams in such a way that they may flash through an opening in the masking plate singly, in pairs, or all three at the same time. After penetrating the plate, the tricolor beams fan out again and strike minute colored phosphor spots coating the glass viewing screen. The microscopic phosphors are spread on the glass in such a manner that one-third of them consist of red dots, one-third green, and one-third blue. These dots light up when struck by an electrical charge.

The electron beam that has been influenced by the incoming red signal falls only on the red spots. The green and blue spots are similarly affected by their respective beams. As the electron beams bearing the primary color signals sweep simultaneously across the phosphor-coated viewing screen, the original televised color scene is reproduced.

Electronics for Travel

Second to its revolutionary effects on communications and military operations in the air, at sea and on land, electronics has brought about profound changes in the field of civilian transportation. Throughout the past thirty years, as knowledge of the science of electronics advanced, important new devices and equipment appeared that added immeasurably to the safety of everyday travel by railroad, steamship, and plane. Air transportation in particular relies heavily on electronics today for the success of its operations.

Aviation Electronics

Navigational aids form one of the biggest groups of electronic equipment for passenger aircraft, as we have glimpsed earlier. Many of those used for commercial flying are the same devices we have discussed in connection with military planes. As engineers continued to perfect equipment for military aircraft, commercial lines began to adapt these electronic aids for their specialized purposes. One of the earliest of the electronic devices for helping airmen find their way through the trackless skies was the radio direction finder, mentioned earlier, which observes by radio signals the direction of a radio sending station.

A similar navigational aid designed mostly for airplanes flying over land routes is the omni-directional radio range. As it exists in the United States, the system involves a network of more than 400 radio transmitters sending out signals of a very high frequency. The omni-range beacon, as the name indicates, sends these signals outward in all directions like the spokes of a wheel. The range of these signals is such that they overlap until the entire country is literally blanketed by them. A pilot flying from one city to another, therefore, has a number of radio routes to choose from to find his objective.

A special receiver is required aboard the airplane to enable the pilot to use the omni-range navigational system. Its principal element is a small cathode-ray tube which provides a visual means of showing whether the airman is on the beam or not. The airborne receiver can also tell the pilot if he is flying toward or away from a particular transmitter beacon. One other help which a flyer can obtain from the omni-directional range system, again with a special receiver, is his distance in miles from a given objective.

We have already seen how radar has been adapted to a blind landing system for bringing aircraft safely down on airfields hemmed in by bad weather. Still another bad weather landing system has been developed which relies exclusively on instruments within the plane activated by electronic equipment at the airport. This is known as the Instrument Landing System, or ILS, and with its use the pilot is completely on his own at all times.

To handle ILS landings, an airfield must be equipped with a number of beacons. First a radio beacon tells the pilot the particular runway on which he must make his landing. A second beacon sends its signals at a precise angle over the center of this runway, the unseen glide path which the airman must maintain in order to touch his wheels down safely. Vertical marker beacons along the length of the runway flash radio signals straight upward, telling the pilot how much of the landing strip has been used up in his touchdown maneuver.

As the airman begins his landing, he watches a meter on his instrument panel which contains two crossed pointers, whose action is controlled by two radio receivers aboard the plane. These pointers show the pilot whether he is to the right or left of the runway, or too high or too low in respect to the glide path beam. This blind landing system has proved itself extremely effective ever since its creation during World War II. GCA and ILS are sometimes combined to help bring airliners to earth. In the not-too-distant future, many aeronautical experts feel, ILS techniques will become an important part of a completely automatic system for controlling the flight of commercial or military air transports. Aircraft will take off, fly a precise air route and land, regardless of the weather conditions, without the assistance of human hands.

One of the most important electronic devices aboard a commercial or military transport plane, aside from navigational instruments, is an automatic pilot. This unit can fly an airplane as well as, if not better than, many human pilots. It consists mainly of a gyroscope, electronic "brain," and servo-mechan-

Heart of a new automatic pilot developed for the U. S. Air Force is this "cageable vertical gyro," an advanced type that never forgets which way is up. *Official Air Force Photo.*

isms which are the muscles of the device for moving the plane's controls.

The gyroscope of the autopilot is fastened to the plane's structure so that the sensitive rotor which it houses will reflect every movement of the plane. As the rotor detects the various motions of the craft, these are sent to and interpreted by an electronic "brain." The latter passes along electrical instructions to servo-mechanisms for properly moving rudder, tail surfaces, ailerons or other elements necessary to keep the plane flying on an even keel. The automatic pilot is a boon to airmen who fly over long distances, since it permits them to relax or concentrate on some other phase of their flight duty.

Commercial airliners, of course, are also equipped with radio-telephones which permit them to maintain contact, throughout much of their sky journey, with their ground bases. Other electronic devices, new or improved varieties, are being produced in a never-ending stream. A few of those available to commercial aircraft include an electronic altimeter, which has proved far more accurate than previous kinds, since it gives an exact measurement between the plane and the earth's surface rather than a simple sea-level reading.

One of the newest electronic radio altimeters sends signals traveling with the speed of light towards the earth's surface.

This panel display gives some idea of the units that go to make up an automatic pilot for aircraft.

These bounce back to the plane, and its altitude is recorded in millionths of a second. The time required for the echoes to return is measured by electronic devices. This data is converted into feet and automatically shows up on the pilot's instrument panel.

The altimeter is so sensitive that it can tell the airman whether he is a few inches from the ground or miles high. A warning light working along with the electronic radio altimeter indicates to the pilot when he is flying below a safe altitude.

A new electronic fuel gauge has been invented that is said to give a far more accurate reading than the conventional flow-meter type. Since fuel consumption is a vital factor on a long-distance flight, the newly developed gauge is expected to be a big help in improving a plane's performance on such aerial journeys.

In addition to the major airlines which fly coast-to-coast and other great distances, there are many smaller companies operating only within restricted areas. These are commonly called feeder lines. Many of the airfields which they use are not as elaborate as the giant terminals located at large cities. In fact, some of the fields are just brief stopping places and often do not have personnel in attendance. This can be a problem for an airman flying a feeder line plane when he wishes to make a landing at night and there is no one at the field to turn on the runway lights. Through the magic of electronics, such situations have become obsolete. Now a pilot can turn on the field lights himself from any point within a distance of 100 miles.

The device which makes this possible operates from the aircraft's transmitter set. The pilot merely pushes a button connected to the "talk" phase of the set three times at one-half second intervals. These pulsed signals are flashed to a receiver at the particular field on which the airman wishes to land, automatically turning on the lights. To turn off the lights, the pilot pushes the same button five times.

All types of transportation have had and will continue to

have a percentage of accidents. Air travel, as we all know, has been no exception to this unhappy record. The cause of every airplane crash is thoroughly investigated with the hope that the information obtained will help reduce the number of others that might occur in the future. But airplane crashes are frequently so destructive that the task of investigators seeking the cause is extremely difficult if not impossible. An airborne electronic tape recording device developed by North American Aviation engineers is expected to help solve this problem.

The recording unit, which weighs eighteen pounds and consists of a number of miniature electronic parts, is protected by a small black crash-proof case, the size of a portable typewriter. The tape measures 1,200 feet in length and is capable of making a verbal log of an air journey up to ten hours in length. The versatility of the recorder is such that it can pick up the pilot's conversation, verbal messages communicated from ground bases, record air pressure data, altitude, length of time the plane has been in the air, vertical climbing speed, normal air speed and direction of flight. In short, it can make a complete record of the plane's journey from take-off to landing.

Years ago, when commercial air travel involved comparatively few flights and passengers, it was an easy matter to handle the business of selling plane tickets. Today, with air transportation approaching a mass basis, this situation has completely

A small, easily-handled airborne recorder to log all important data on flights of missiles or airplanes for as long as 10 hours. *North American Aviation, Inc.*

changed. Ticket agents are hard-pressed to keep track of the constantly changing picture of flight reservations resulting from the volume demand for airplane seats. Electronics has been called upon to increase the speed and efficiency of this phase of airline operations. One step in this direction was the Magnetronic Reservisor, developed jointly by American Airlines and the Teleregister Corporation.

Desk sets such as this are hooked up to the Reservisor and used by travel agents. *American Airlines.*

Broadly speaking, the Reservisor is a magnetic and electronic device for taking care of seat reservations. Actually, however, it is a high-speed computer, a storage and filing system, a data transmission instrument, a display device, and a recording unit all rolled into one. Because of these multiple features, ticket agents scattered over a wide area have ready access to a large inventory of available seats on many flights, and can change this inventory record as seats are reserved or canceled.

The heart of the Reservisor consists of two drums whose surface is covered with tiny areas of magnetized material. These store the inventory data as to seats available on various flights. A complicated electronic arrangement can place such information on the drum or remove it and interpret the data they con-

These rotating storage drums are the "memory" portion of the Reservisor's electronic "brain." *American Airlines.*

tain. The drums revolve at 1,200 R.P.M. The Reservisor is placed at a central location and is connected by a wire hook-up to offices of ticket agents scattered over a wide section of a city.

On the ticket agent's counter is a unit that looks like a small adding machine. Several rows of buttons line its surface which are related to the days of the month and the number of seats. There is also a slot at one end in which the ticket agent drops a small metal plate. The latter contains a portion of the complete schedule of the airline company's flights. Fewer than fifty of these plates are needed by the ticket seller to get information on any one of nearly three thousand flights a day. If one, for

This is the electronic "brain" of the Reservisor. *American Airlines.*

example, were to ask for two reservations for Chicago tomorrow, the agent would drop the correct destination plate into the slot, punch the buttons corresponding to tomorrow's date and two seats and then flip a switch. With lightning-like swiftness small lamps in front of the plate would light up. These carry the responses of the "brain."

The agent immediately knows what seats are available and for what flight—eight, ten or twelve o'clock. Selecting the eight o'clock flight, let us assume, the ticket seller then proceeds to push down on the lamp in front of the 8:00 A.M. section of the destination plate, flips a switch to put out the lights, and flips another switch which is marked "sell." Again the response is immediate and now the lamp in front of the 10:00 A.M. section only lights up. A larger, green lamp marked "check" also lights up and this tells the agent that the reservations have been secured, and two seats are removed from the inventory on the drums.

If a cancellation has to be made, the agent goes through the same procedure as for selling a ticket with the result that this time two seats are added to the memory drums.

Railroad Electronics

Although railroads have not quite reached the extent that airlines have in adapting electronics for their operations, they nevertheless do make considerable use of such equipment. What is more important, this use of new or improved apparatus is increasing constantly. We have already seen how much electronics has meant toward improving communications on railroad systems. Now railroad engineers are going further and acquiring electronic equipment for many other important jobs. One of the more interesting of these is an electronic control system for checking at a central point the arrival of an approaching train.

This particular piece of electronic equipment, called the Watcher, was developed by the Erie Railroad and placed in operation on a section of their route in New York State. It automatically identifies certain trains and records their numbers and arrival times on paper.

The robot Watcher consists of an identifying coil beneath the caboose of a freight train, a weatherproof coil fixed to a track at a particular point along the railroad route, and a control machine installed in the dispatcher's office. This makes a record in ink on a moving tape of the information sent by the Watcher. When this indicates that the train has passed the control point, the dispatcher then knows that that particular section of track is clear and he can permit an opposing or following train to go through.

The caboose coil is wire wound in such a way that it indicates a particular train like Train Number I or II or III. Different winding patterns are used for different trains.

The robot coil fixed between the tracks is connected to an electrical source and acts like a radio transmitter. The transmitter begins to operate automatically when a locomotive approaches. Long before the caboose reaches it, the transmitter is "on the air."

The caboose coil picks up the "radio waves" and carries them through its particular pattern of windings. The waves are then returned to the receiving unit of the track device. The distinctive signal that has been received is instantly sent by wire to the control machine in the dispatcher's office. A light on this equip-

An inert coil, mounted under the caboose, is the heart of an electronic train identification system. *Photo courtesy Erie Railroad.*

ment tells whether it was train number I, II, III, or IV. Also at that moment one of four pens drawing parallel lines on a moving tape shifts to the right. This shows that the train has cleared the track. Each of these pens is assigned to a particular train, and while it is working, the others remain still. They become activated only when they receive the electrical impulses from their own particular coil pattern. The paper tape is printed with hour and minute lines so that a permanent record of the train's signal is recorded.

The robot Watcher is said to have countless possibilities in addition to the one just described. For example, it could be used for opening and closing switches after specific trains have passed. It might turn on lights at unattended passenger stations where a lone train may be scheduled to stop in the middle of the night. In short, the Watcher is pioneering the time when many railroad operations will be done almost completely by electronic robots.

Marine Electronics

Ships at sea have long made use of radio and electronic equipment to improve the safety and efficiency of their operations. One of the first electronic devices which they adopted was for communication purposes. This was shortly after Marconi had demonstrated his wireless telegraphy invention to the world in 1896. The crews and passengers of many a foundering ship have owed their lives to the magic of radio. Since that distant era communication apparatus for sea-going vessels has steadily expanded and improved. Radio telegraph transmitters have become more powerful, increasing the range and clarity of radio signals; receivers have become more sensitive, and much of the overall equipment automatic. Radio-telephone has also made its appearance on ships, express liners mostly, so that passengers can communicate with any point on shore as well as from ship to ship.

Of equal importance with communication, electronics has

165

furnished gyroscopic-pilots for steering super liners, and apparatus for helping mariners with their navigational problems. Among the first of these were radio beacons placed in operation along the shores of the United States in the 1920's. These beacons are located on lightships, at lighthouses, and more recently they have been installed in marker buoys at the entrances to harbors. The beacons send out precisely timed radio signals in all directions. They also have other distinguishing characteristics from other beacons. With the help of special radio direction-finding equipment aboard ship, a navigator can easily determine his bearing in relation to the beacon by the incoming signals. This operates much the same way as for aircraft. On many occasions the radio beacon navigation system has enabled ships to make port in severe fog.

Electronic marine navigation aids were advanced tremendously during World War II. We have already taken note of how much radar has meant to the safety of ships and passengers especially at night and when the weather has turned bad. Another wartime development which has proved itself of equal value is Loran. This is a long-range system of navigation by radio waves providing accurate lines of position at sea by measurement of the time-difference in pulse transmission.

Loran is a newly coined word standing for LO-ng RA-nge N-avigation. It was developed principally by the scientists and engineers at the Radiation Laboratory during World War II. The system consists of pairs of accurately located radio trans-

This is a radio-beacon buoy. The whip-like antenna sends out radio impulses which are picked up by the navigators of an approaching ship. *Official Coast Guard Photo.*

166

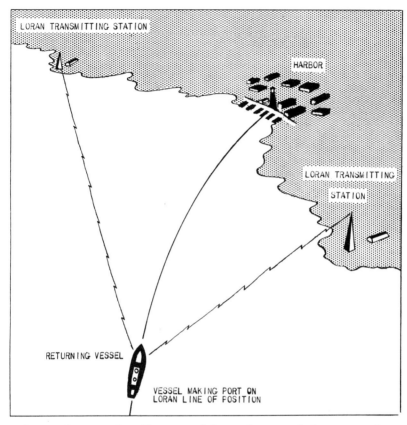

LORAN TRANSMITTING STATION

HARBOR

LORAN TRANSMITTING
STATION

RETURNING VESSEL

VESSEL MAKING PORT ON
LORAN LINE OF POSITION

mitters along a shoreline, special receivers and Loran navigational charts aboard a ship.

The transmitters operate in twos and send out their signals in the form of short pulses. The transmitter that starts the process is called the "master" and the second is known as the "slave." This is because the "master" tells the "slave" when to send its own signal through the air. The Loran pulses are in the form of brief bursts of electrical energy, similar to the microwave pulse of radar. The wavelengths of Loran radio signals, however, are much longer than those for radar. Loran has a range of 700 miles during the day and 1,400 miles at night.

167

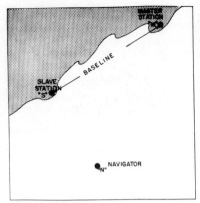 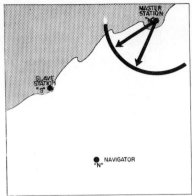

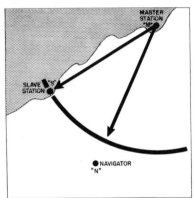 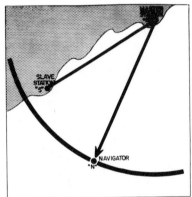

Sequence of Operation of Loran Transmitting Stations. Step I. Navigator aboard ship at "N" is within range of stations "M" and "S" and is about to receive Loran signals.

Step II. Loran transmission cycle is begun by "master" station. Pulse is radiated in all directions and travels toward both "slave" station and navigator.

Step III. Pulse transmitted by "master" station arrives at "slave" but has not yet reached the navigator.

Step IV. Pulse from "master" station arrives at position of navigator. "Slave" station has already received "master" pulse and is waiting for proper amount of time to elapse before transmitting to assure correct synchronization with "master."

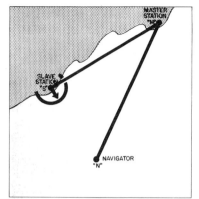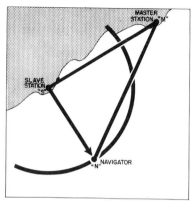

Step V. After waiting for the proper amount of time to assure correct synchronization the "slave" transmits its pulse. The navigator has already received the pulse from the "master" station.

Step VI. "Slave" pulse arrives at navigator's position. Since navigator has already received the signal from the "master" station, Loran reading is taken by measuring the time elapsed between the arrival of the master and slave pulses. After both signals have traveled throughout their effective range, the cycle is repeated.

Aboard ship a receiver containing a cathode-ray tube detects these Loran signals in visual form and with the aid of a precise timing device is able to determine the difference in the times of their arrival. This measured time-difference is then applied to specially prepared charts which allow the navigator to find a line of position on the earth's surface. When a second line of position is obtained from another pair of Loran stations and the intersections of the two lines noted, the navigator is able to find exactly the ship's position in relation to its destination.

This long-range electronic navigation system, incidentally, is also being used by commercial airplanes flying over the ocean routes between the American and European continents. Loran transmitters have been established on all three coasts of the United States and at many points throughout the world. This long-range navigational arrangement is said to have a number of advantages over others that have been developed in that the

Navigator aboard ship obtaining positional data from a Loran receiver indicator. Note Loran chart and tables on work shelf. *Official U. S. Coast Guard Photo.*

navigator can obtain a "fix" on his whereabouts in from two to three minutes. Furthermore, its accuracy is extremely high, equal to that of celestial observations, and it can operate regardless of the weather conditions. Loran, with the aid of other types of electronic apparatus, is making the life of those who go down to the sea in ships far easier than in pre-electronic eras.

Smaller work boats such as tugs, towboats and other craft that sail harbors, rivers and lakes have also benefited from the magic of electronics. Two-way radio-telephone communications and radar have been the most outstanding of this equipment so far. A new electronic device called a Lever Pilot, when hooked up to a vessel's radar, will steer it automatically and with great accuracy. The electronic pilot may also be used independently of radar, particularly when visibility is good.

CHAPTER FIVE

VERSATILE ELECTRONS

There is hardly a phase of the industrial world today that does not in some manner or degree make use of the magic of electronics. All the miraculous offshoots of electronics, including X-rays, television, phototubes, microwaves, dielectrics, infrared rays, and ultra-violet rays, are involved in this great, progressing industrial revolution. The range of their applications runs all the way from food processing industries to fabricators of heavy steel products.

Food Inspection and Preparation

In many states where food is raised and prepared for market, the government maintains an inspection service to see that the processors use foods or fruits that measure up to the prescribed standards. A case in point is tomatoes. State inspectors are on hand at canning establishments to see that properly ripened tomatoes are used in the canning process. One way to judge the ripeness of tomatoes is to cut one in half and compare the shading with special color charts. But the results of this method have not always been satisfactory. An electronic device called an Agtron has been developed which places tomato inspection on a much more accurate basis.

The Agtron is a box-like affair filled with electronic circuits, phototubes, and light filters. It is fitted with a sliding drawer in which the cut tomato halves are placed. These are laid in cup-like holders mounted on a spring and pressed up against a fine wire screen. While in this position, the tomato halves are scanned by phototubes first through red filters and then green. A comparison of the reflecting intensity of the halves of the tomato helps determine their ripeness. A meter on the face of the grading instrument marked "Well Colored," "Fairly Well

The Agtron, an electronic instrument for judging the ripeness of tomatoes.

Colored," and "Below Color" gives a visual reading of the scanning results.

The Agtron weighs 65 pounds, has handles attached to its casing, and is easily transportable. Its inventors feel that it will be just as effective for grading other vegetables, too. It has proved itself so superior to the human-eye technique that more than 150 of them have been put into operation in California alone.

Another problem of the food-canning industry is the need to know the contents of cans after they have been passed through a cooker and prepared for labeling. The difficulty lies in the fact that a variety of foods are sent through the cooker at one time. To solve this, a group of California electronic engineers have come up with an electronic device that can tell exactly the contents of the cans.

Before the food is placed in cans, magnetized spots are placed on the bottom of the containers in one of nine different patterns. Each pattern represents a particular food. The cans are filled, sealed, and passed through the cooker in the usual way. As they emerge, the cans are whirled at a high speed of 3,600 revolutions per minute beside a battery of coils. With the help of the magnetic spots, an alternating current is created which passes on to an analyzer. This unit is capable of interpreting the particular pattern of spots on each container. Once their identity is made known, the cans are separated and move along conveyor belts into their respective divisions for proper labeling.

In the far northwest of the United States walnut growers have acquired an electronic nutcracker that has helped to boost their shelled walnut production by more than 30 per cent. The equipment consists of a battery of box-like units called capacitors. These store up electrical energy and then release it in 65,000 volt bursts 20 times a second. The powerful electrical impulses are distributed to eighteen individual cracking machines into which the walnuts are individually fed. As each of the nuts is exposed to the miniature lightning bolts, their shell is blown off with little or no damage to the nutmeat. The automatic

A line of electronic walnut-cracking machines. Air ducts overhead remove ionized air and fine dust. Entire room is sheathed with aluminum plating and building is grounded 32 feet underground. *Walnut Growers Assoc.*

electronic nutcracker can handle 1,200 pounds of walnuts an hour, almost twice the capacity of other equipment.

The electronic devices mentioned so far are just a tiny fraction of those used in the food industry and its allied lines. In the food packaging field, automatic electronic apparatus exists that weighs each box of food as it moves along a conveyor belt checking to see whether it is properly filled. In soft-drink plants devices based on the photoelectric eye are used to check the liquids for any foreign matter. Employing instruments based on X-rays, candy manufacturers inspect the sealed boxes of their sweets to see that no unwanted object has found its way inside. Using similar X-ray equipment, grain processors inspect their product to determine if it is infested with weevil and whether it is fit for use in foods.

Other electronic devices that make use of cathode rays are being tried out for sterilizing food products, particularly in the bakery line. The rays destroy organisms that create moldy and decayed conditions and permit the foods to remain fresh and appetizing for longer periods of time. Another type of ray, the

An electronic control indicator for gauging the correct weight of the contents of packages. *Battelle Memorial Institute.*

174

ultra-violet variety, is being employed in the dairy industry to impart vitamin D to dairy products. As food processors learn further about the wonders of electrons, they are acquiring new and more amazing equipment to safeguard better the health of consumers and to make their operations more efficient.

Electronics for Metal Products

The metal products industry, including both the makers of light and heavy goods, has long been applying electronics for improving many of its varied operations. X-ray equipment was among the first of the electronic aids which industry acquired to help produce better products. Once it was found that penetrating X-rays could see through inanimate as well as animate matter, they were looked upon as an excellent means for inspecting metals for hidden flaws. X-ray inspection of metals saw its initial large-scale use during World War I. This role of detective was the first job which X-rays took over in industry. They have long since proved their worth and are considered almost an indispensable part of factory equipment.

One company, Alcoa, placed its first X-ray metal inspection machine in operation twenty-five years ago. Today, it has been estimated that close to 4,000 manufacturing plants use this

Making an X-ray diffraction pattern of aluminum sheet to determine its crystalline structure. *Aluminum Company of America.*

175

A 250,000-volt industrial X-ray unit being positioned for inspection of large metal casting. *General Electric Co., X-Ray Division.*

electronic servant in some form. The reason for the industrial X-ray machine's great popularity is easily undersood by the fact that they save the companies using them thousands of dollars. By spotting unseen flaws in metal stock before the latter is turned into a finished product, X-ray inspectors help reduce the amount of rejected finished goods.

X-ray equipment used in industry ranges from small portable units to giant immovable machines. Some of the larger ones use as many as 24,000,000 volts, producing deep-piercing X-rays to probe thick slabs of steel. The Ford Motor Car Company employs a machine of this kind that can spot pin holes in steel forgings more than 12″ thick.

At the opposite extreme is a newly developed unit, comparatively a midget, using only a fraction of the voltage. Known as the Resotron 250, this industrial X-ray machine was developed by the General Electric Company.

The Resotron 250 is less than 15″ in diameter and measures 44″ in length. It weighs a mere 150 pounds as compared to 1,150-pound types designed to do the same kind of work. One of its versatile features is its ability to take pictures "inside out." This is made possible by a special protruding "snout" through which the X-rays are flashed. Workmen preparing to inspect the weld joint connecting two sections of pipe, for example, can place the X-ray unit inside the pipe and alter its exposure area without disturbing the pipe. In the same way it may also be

The Resotron, a compact and highly maneuverable miniature X-ray machine is being placed in position inside a pressure boiler. *General Electric Co., X-Ray Division.*

inserted in large castings or in areas ordinarily difficult to reach.

The midget X-ray machine is operated with from 75,000 to 250,000 volts and can be used on metals ranging from magnesium to steel. Despite its small size, the Resotron is capable of penetrating steel up to $3\frac{1}{2}''$ thick. It is expected to have wide usefulness in foundries, welding shops, shipyards, and on building and pipeline projects. The X-ray unit is already being employed effectively in United States Navy shipyards, where it is inspecting critical welded seams and stressed areas on submarines and other ships in the process of repair or construction.

In more recent years the metal industry has discovered that X-ray equipment can be developed and used for purposes other than those of inspection. One of the more important is as a gauge for measuring the thickness of coating material on sheet steel. To check the quality of their tin plate product, the United States Steel Corporation has created a custom-made X-ray measuring machine that combines both a conventional X-ray unit and a Geiger counter. The Geiger counter is more familiar as a device for detecting the existence of radioactive substances. In this particular machine, however, it serves a different purpose—it measures reflected X-rays.

Tin plate is made from very thin sheet steel and then coated on both sides with tin. Two processes are employed in its manufacture. One is known as the electroplating method and the other the "hot dip." The latter is the older process and is used mostly when heavier coatings of various thickness for different types of cans are required. Sheet steel, first cut to standard dimensions, is dipped in a bath of molten tin. The problem involved with this process is the control of the thickness of tin coating.

To determine this measurement, a sheet of tin plate is exposed briefly to an X-ray beam. The Geiger counter attached to the gauge simultaneously measures the reflected rays that strike the steel sheet beneath. Some of the reflected X-rays are absorbed by the tin coating. The remainder are picked up by the Geiger counter which, because of the mathematical relationship between the X-rays soaked up by the tin coating and those reflected by the steel beneath, can record with great precision the thickness of the tin.

To prevent the tin coating from becoming thicker on one side of the metal than the other, the gauging apparatus has two measuring heads which move about on both sides of the sheet at the same time. Push-button controls start the instrument's operation. Within thirty seconds the gauge shuts off automatically and the exact readings of the thickness are shown on printed moving paper tapes. Its margin of error is estimated at less than six ten-millionths of an inch. Its speed and accuracy make it superior to the older chemical method used for this measuring operation.

Cellophane and Plastics

An adhesive-tape manufacturer employs a similar X-ray machine to determine both the thickness of the cellophane paper base of his product and the infinitely thin twin layers of adhesive. An X-ray detecting instrument of quite another nature is used by breweries and food-canning companies to determine whether the cans are properly filled. As the cans move along a conveyor belt, a beam of X-rays is shot through a container near

178

the top end. If it strikes a can with empty space above the contents, the X-rays beam flashes through to the opposite side and strikes a sensitive detector unit. The detector in turn sets off a chain of activity resulting in a strong blast of air that topples the defective product from the conveyor line.

Although not involved with any industrial activity at the moment, another novel X-ray application just emerging from the experimental stage is that of "curing" plastics. A powerful beam of electrons from a million-volt X-ray machine has been found by General Electric scientists to toughen flexible plastic material such as that used for certain containers so that they can

After exposure to the electron bombardment from a million-volt X-ray machine, flexible plastic bottles can stand up under steam sterilization that makes them suitable for the first time as containers for pharmaceuticals and biological fluids. *General Electric Company.*

withstand the withering effects of steam sterilization. The electron beam bombardment periods last but a few seconds and solidifies only a portion of the liquid plastic. Products made from the toughened plastic material are expected to enjoy more widespread use, especially among drug manufacturers, to hold pharmaceuticals and biological fluids such as blood plasma normally placed in bulky, fragile glass containers.

Photoelectric Tubes

One of the most widely used electronic applications in industry involves devices that depend for their operation on the magic of photoelectric tubes. Most of us are familiar with this electronic wonder in the form of having doors open before us as though by some unseen hand, or fountains spout water without any assistance. As we have noted in a previous chapter, these tubes are sensitive to variations in light intensity with the result that they can induce an electric current to flow. The latter, in turn, can then be applied to do a variety of jobs. Taking advantage of their basically simple operation, engineers have developed scores of different industrial devices and equipment that run the full range of versatility. Operations calling for sight, feeling, sorting, controlling, counting and even smelling, are all represented by these electronic servants.

The door-opening action performed by a photoelectric tube or "electric eye," as it is better known, is as good an example as any for explaining how such electronic equipment operates. In this particular application a beam of light is flashed across a pathway and accurately focused on a photoelectric tube directly opposite. As long as the beam remains on the tube, an electric current is produced which operates a series of relays and other devices that hold the door closed. However, just as soon as the beam is broken, as happens when a person crosses through it, the flow of current released by the tube is stopped. This condition starts another series of devices, operated by air or a combined electric-mechanical force such as servo-mechanisms, that push the door open. This is a comparatively simple chore of which the photoelectric tube is capable. There are many more, some of them extremely complex.

Another type of photoelectric device used for checking tasks

This electronic instrument, called a Proximity Meter, can measure or compare dimensions and distortions which were previously impossible to obtain by mechanical means. It can gauge the concentricity of shafts and rotors, serve as a micrometer to measure very small dimensions or as a device for measuring the thickness of paint. *Fielden Instrument Division.*

is that which determines color values in relation to certain desired standards. This instrument has widespread use in a number of fields and exists in various forms and under various names. Some are known as photometers, other as colorimeters, while still another group goes under the name of color comparators. Despite the different names with which they are identified, all these checking instruments operate fundamentally in the same way and aim for the same result—to check products for their correct color values.

Typical of the instruments in this color checking group is the electronic comparator. It uses two beams of light, one of which is focused through or made to reflect from a standard color sample to a photoelectric tube. The other beam is focused on the sample shade of color being checked and is reflected to another phototube. The two photoelectric tubes are hooked up to a galvanometer that indicates whether the tubes are receiving the same amount of radiating intensity from the colors being tested. This electronic color checking instrument is widely employed in the textile industry, by paint manufacturers and in some food-processing plants.

Closed-Circuit Television

One of the latest and probably most imaginative applications of electronics to industrial activity is the use of television. This is not quite like the home television we all know, but rather

The "TV-Eye" is a compact, closed-circuit television system recently developed by the Radio Corporation of America. *RCA Victor.*

182

severely limited in its operation. In fact, because of its restricted nature it is commonly referred to as a closed-circuit television system. Not only is its transmission and reception confined to a single, specially assigned channel, but it is normally kept within the bounds of a single structure. However, as TV's valuable services are becoming more widely appreciated, its range of usefulness is also increasing. Some companies with more than one plant have closed-circuit TV systems connecting their various buildings.

The closed-circuit TV hook-up is based on a small, portable TV camera and transmission unit. This apparatus views a particular factory operation and sends it out over a single channel to some remote receiving point. At the latter end of the system is a control device and monitor receiving set. This can be tuned just as simply as home receivers. Incidentally, the channel assigned for a restricted TV system is a free one and does not interfere with any of those already established for public use. A closed-circuit TV receiver cannot pick up any of these outside channels.

When closed-circuit television systems were first tried out, they required a large viewing camera and a great deal of extra equipment for transmission purposes. This has been largely changed now as a result of improvements brought about by the Allen B. Du Mont Laboratories and the Radio Corporation of America. Both these companies have developed portable industrial TV camera units described as revolutionary compared to previous equipment.

Du Mont's, for example, called the Tel-Eye, is a completely self-contained camera unit that has all the necessary means for viewing a scene and transmitting it over a private wire. Its size is comparable to that of a portable typewriter case, and it is easily moved about. The Tel-Eye is said to be extremely simple and efficient in operation. It can be used with any standard very high frequency TV receiver by simply plugging the Tel-Eye unit in a standard wall socket and hooking up the camera's output cable to the TV receiver. The camera transmission equipment is able to send pictures to more than one receiving set at distances up to 2,000 feet. Tel-Eye weighs eighteen pounds and is powered by seventeen tubes. Standard TV camera chains are usually made up of five pieces of equipment with a total of 118 tubes and weigh in the neighborhood of 350 pounds. This is a good illustration of how electronics engineers have advanced in their understanding of the behavior and control of electrons.

RCA's industrial TV camera unit is of a similar compact nature and is called the TV-Eye. The camera and control unit are separate but portable. The camera weighs four pounds and is equipped with a Vidicon picture-taking tube measuring 1″ in diameter and 6″ in length. The TV-Eye is also simple to operate, especially since the camera does not have any working controls.

A typical application of an industrial closed-circuit TV hookup is that of the Ford Motor Company's Buffalo plant where

TV installation at the Ford Motor Company's Buffalo stamping plant. Baler operator in plant watches progress of loading on TV screen at control board and moves gondola by remote control as car is filled. *Ford Motor Company.*

In the first installation of its kind, a television camera, monitor and receiver have been set up in the 80-inch hot strip mill at the United States Steel Corporation's Gary Sheet and Tin Mill plant. Operator can watch progress of steel strip and spot potential trouble. *United States Steel Corporation.*

automobile body parts are made. The TV camera is focused on a chute down which bales of steel trimmings tumble into a gondola railroad car. The receiving set is 300′ away inside the plant where an operator watching the screen continuously observes conditions outdoors. By pressing a series of buttons on his remote control board, the lone worker can regulate the movement of the baled steel trimmings, load them into freight cars, and even move empty cars into position as the loaded ones are rolled away. His TV camera eye tells him when the cars are filled.

A steel-making plant has found the industrial television system of equal value. During one of its many operations, white hot molten metal is made to flow from the spout of a furnace into a mold. Hot, burning sparks fly in all directions as this pouring action takes place, but the operator stands off at a safe distance of about 50 feet. The secret of the technique is a television camera suspended from a special frame directly above the mold. As the molten metal pours into the form, the TV camera eye watches the action and reports to the distant operator by means of his viewing screen when the mold is full. Remote controls permit the steel worker to tilt the furnace upright, stop the pouring and prepare for the next mold.

Incidentally, the TV equipment used in this heavy industry operation is often different from that normally used. The camera tube is of the image dissector type rather than the image orthicon. This tube does not have the usual cathode or electron gun, but a very complicated element called an electron multiplier, which enables it to capture and transmit images. In addition to its use in steel plants, this type of TV camera tube is

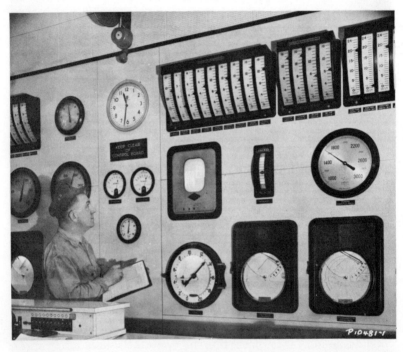

In a boiler control room at the Waterside electric generating station of Consolidated Edison Company, an operator checks boiler water level readings on television screen. Coaxial cables link the camera, at the station's fourth floor level, with the boiler control room on the operating floor about 90 feet below. A bi-color gauge is used so that the TV image, which appears on a 10-inch screen set into the boiler control panel, shows a distinct separation between water and steam. The light-sensitive elements in the pick-up tube are affected by color, red appearing as pale gray, and green as near-black. *Consolidated Edison Company of New York, Inc.*

186

also finding itself reporting on the conditions within power-plant boilers, watching freight sidings and checking on smoke issuing from industrial chimneys.

Electric power companies no less than product manufacturers have put the industrial TV system to good use. For example, in Consolidated Edison's huge generating plant in Manhattan, television serves as a continuous monitor, bringing views of otherwise hard-to-see locations to personnel in a central boiler-control room. On one screen in particular an operator is able to keep a constant eye on gauges that show the water level in the boilers. This is an important task since a boiler's water level is a critical factor in high-pressure boiler operations. In this case the TV camera and receiver are a big help because the main boiler being watched is about 200′ directly above the control room. The TV camera is focused on the boiler's water-level gauge and the picture it views is sent via a coaxial cable to a

A television camera aimed at the water-level gauge on one of the boilers at Consolidated Edison Company's Waterside electric generating station in Manhattan transmits gauge readings by coaxial cable to a television screen in the boiler control room on the station's operating floor, some 90 feet below.

receiver in the control room. The operator can easily keep tabs on the gauge readings and make the proper adjustments if necessary. Prior to television, a system of mirrors was employed to relay the image of the gauge down to the control point.

Still another important task is being carried out by closed-circuit TV at this electric power plant and that is to report on the smoke issuing from the stacks several hundred feet high. By observing the stacks, an operator can tell whether his boilers are working at their most efficient peak. A puff of smoke may indicate to him that there is trouble of some kind inside the boiler. In the case of this Consolidated Edison plant, a TV camera is mounted on another of their buildings several blocks away and pointed at the stacks. An automatic mechanism keeps the camera lens properly adjusted at all times regardless of the

A television camera, aimed at the stacks atop the Waterside electric generating station of Consolidated Edison Company in Manhattan from another company building several blocks away, transmits the picture by coaxial cable to a TV screen in one of Waterside's boiler control rooms. *Consolidated Edison of New York, Inc.*

188

sunlight intensity, thus assuring a good picture at all times. The images viewed by the camera are transmitted, again by coaxial cable, to the control room, where if the characteristics of the smoke coming out of the stacks indicate trouble, proper adjustments can be made in an instant.

A similar closed-circuit TV system is being used by a savings bank to speed up operations between its main office and a branch almost forty blocks away. The New York Savings Bank has found that by utilizing a private TV installation between its two offices, along with computing and other electronic equipment, it needs less space for its branch office. Further, the TV hook-up reduces the number of necessary employees while at

Closed-circuit TV being used for banking operations. *The New York Savings Bank.*

the same time increasing efficiency. The teller's cage is equipped with a small TV screen. If a withdrawal is made, the TV unit is used to check quickly the person's bank balance and signature from records at the main office.

The examples of closed-circuit television discussed so far by no means cover the full range of its versatility. The private TV system is employed with equal success beyond industry, in atomic energy plants where many dangerous operations can be safely viewed and controlled at a distance. A variation of this type of TV equipment is used for underwater tasks in checking on the condition of pilings of docks and wharves. Scientists have also employed underwater television for inspecting oyster beds.

An engineer of the Argonne National Laboratory (Atomic Energy) performing remote control operations by the use of three-dimensional television. *Argonne National Laboratory.*

190

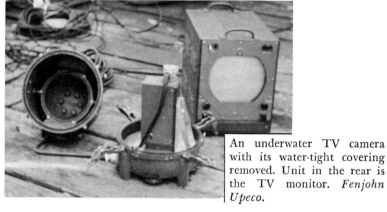

An underwater TV camera with its water-tight covering removed. Unit in the rear is the TV monitor. *Fenjohn Upeco.*

But perhaps the most popular of the non-industrial uses of closed-circuit TV systems is in the field of education. Its adoption by some colleges is enabling students at the back of lecture halls to get a close-up view of a demonstration being performed by a professor. In medical schools it is serving to excellent advantage by allowing large numbers of future doctors to view

Television as a classroom aid. Here a Vidicon TV camera attached to a conventional light microscope picks up the image of the magnified specimen on the slide in the microscope and enlarges it further on the screen of the TV receiver. The entire class is thus able to see the bacteria which the lecturer is discussing. *RCA Victor.*

191

close-up operations being performed by skilled, experienced surgeons. In military training it speeds up the instruction of its personnel, especially in technical subjects. The educational potential of private TV systems, like the industrial, is finding newer applications with each passing day.

Law enforcement agencies are beginning to adapt television to their specialized activities. The New York Police Department, for one, has recently experimented by televising the questioning period of prisoners at the main headquarters to outlying police stations within the city. After it is perfected and established, this TV system should prove helpful in enabling larger numbers of policemen to be briefed on criminals than with current methods. TV is also being installed in jails to keep particular watch on the behavior of belligerent prisoners.

Heating Processes

As we have seen in a previous chapter, one of the important radiations of electrons is the infra-red ray. This heat-bearing electronic energy has also been found helpful for a variety of industrial chores, especially in processes where quick, thorough drying is essential, such as drying the paint on new automobiles.

New type infra-red lamp developed by General Electric. The new lamp is in the form of quartz tubes rather than the conventional glass bulbs. Tubes of 1,000 and 500 watts are shown in comparison to a king-size cigarette. The revolutionary lamp is expected to be used for heating, baking, cooking and drying. *General Electric Company.*

Freshly painted cars are placed beneath banks of lamps which are specially made to produce infra-red rays. Each lamp is fitted with a reflector to intensify the heat-bearing rays. These electromagnetic radiations quickly dry paint from the inside outward. Since mass production is the automobile manufacturer's stock in trade, speed is an important factor in his operations.

Pottery makers are also using infra-red rays to speed up the drying phase of their pottery-making operations. One dinnerware manufacturer, using long infra-red rays rather than the customary short type, has found that his products leave the molds in a more uniform manner, do not become warped nor crack while going through their final processing. The pottery is placed on a large rectangular metal mat under the tubular all-metal electric radiant heaters. The baking period is very brief.

Another form of electronic heating widely used by industry is known as dielectric heating. The word dielectric refers to materials that are non-conductors of electricity, which include almost all substances that are not metallic. Because of this characteristic of certain materials, electrical energy can be applied to them to accomplish specific manufacturing chores, such as sealing, curing, or shaping. This electrical force, in the form of radio frequency waves, is applied to the product usually by metal plates and a powerful electronic generator. The plates, normally placed on opposite sides of the substance being treated, become energized by powerful quantities of these radio waves. Intense heat results from this electronic action which occurs within the material.

The rubber industry employs dielectric heating equipment for sealing operations on many of their products. Plastic manufacturers likewise use it to fasten different parts of their plastic goods together. The food industry also makes extensive use of this electronic heating apparatus for sterilizing wheat and dehydrating different kinds of food. Bakers treat their bread with dielectric heating to prevent the formation of mold. Processors of peanuts, coffee and cocoa beans all use this heating method for treating their products. One of the most popular fields in which dielectric heating is applied is the wood industry.

Many lumber suppliers, furniture makers and boat builders have adopted this electronic heating equipment to improve their products and to speed manufacturing operations. When applied in curing green lumber, for example, the process takes about fifteen hours. The older curing method requires a month. Not only does dielectric heating make for a shorter curing period but it is said to improve the quality of the lumber by freeing it of warping tendencies. Plywood manufacturers have found dielectric heating an ideal method for gluing the various layers of veneer together far better than by the usual techniques, with the time element reduced from hours to minutes.

What might be described as a twin-brother to dielectric heating, employed mostly with metals, is called induction heating. It operates in a slightly different fashion. The part being treated usually has a coil of copper wire or tubing placed around or near it. This is connected to an electronic generator which causes radio-frequencies to originate from the coil. As these waves make their way through the metal, by a process known as induction, extreme heat is created. Metal working plants usually employ this electronic aid for heat-treating or toughening metals. Its application can be confined to a small area, which often makes induction-heating a preferred method.

Sound Waves in Industry.

Earlier we mentioned ultrasonics as an extremely new branch of physical science that owes much of its existence to electronic developments. At least, many of the devices currently being used to create these ultra-high sound waves are basically electronic. And just as with purely electronic equipment or instruments, industry is discovering that ultrasonics has many practical uses. Electronic oscillators are frequently employed to start the cycle of ultra-high frequency sound waves in many devices producing them for industrial purposes. The electrical energy first created is transformed into mechanical vibrations by other elements in such equipment and then radiated in the form of ultrasonics.

As a blender of liquids, whether chemicals, foods or metal alloys, ultrasonic equipment has proved that it has few equals. It has also been successfully applied to speeding up the aging process of spirits and wine. In the research field ultrasonics has shown that it can directly affect bacteria, either destroying or stimulating them. One large aircraft manufacturer has found ultrasonic equipment to be a valuable tool for inspecting forgings. Coupled with an oscilloscope, the instrument sends its ultra-high frequency sound waves through forgings immersed in water, and by measuring the time it takes for the sound to travel through the piece being inspected, flaws can be detected. Flaws show up as "pips" on the oscilloscope screen. The apparatus has a high degree of accuracy so that operators can spot flaws in forgings smaller than the size of a pinhead.

An even more recent development has been the creation of an ultrasonic electronic machine tool that can easily drill or shape super-hard materials. Some of the hardest known—tungsten, silicon carbides and boron—can be embossed or cut to slight depths within minutes. The tool employs sound vibrations of more than one and a half million per minute. It is expected to play an important part in the die-making field which normally uses extremely hard materials. The developers of this tool even feel that ultimately it can be adapted for dentistry in drilling tooth cavities.

Automatic Devices

One of the overall effects of the application of electronics to industry is the development of factories that are becoming more and more self-operating. Many of the monotonous, systematic operations in manufacturing plants are being taken over by electronic "brains" and mechanical muscles. Industrial engineers who are vitally concerned with making factory operations ever more efficient, have coined the word "Automation" to describe this progressing development. The automotive industry is one of the leaders in this technical march of progress. A number of manufacturing plants in that field are already well on the road to becoming the automatic factory of the future. The Cleveland plant of the Ford Motor Company is an excellent example of this modern industrial trend.

This huge auto factory has been equipped with a large number of electronic units that automatically gather great quantities of technical information, make decisions and then send out messages to scores of machines that do the actual work. The electronic "brains" direct giant steel arms and fingers to pick

A portion of the electronic equipment used to transform a conventional industrial plant into one that is almost completely automatic in its operation. Photo shows typical installation of overhead central control panel for inline machine tool at the Ford Motor Company's Cleveland engine plant. Under the panel is a progressive station-to-station crankshaft drilling machine. *Ford Motor Company.*

196

up, turn over, or shift pieces as large as 180-pound engine blocks. These electronic robots, some of which measure 96′ in length and weigh 140,000 pounds, receive their information from dozens of switches or electrical "scouts" strategically placed throughout the plant.

Rough castings of motor blocks enter the production line at one end and emerge at the other after going through a dozen or more automatic-electronic mechanical processes with hardly a human touch. One might suppose that such a factory will result in the loss of jobs for human workers. But those who are directing this industrial development say no. Instead of pushing buttons to start an army of self-operating machines, workers will concentrate on tasks that will increase the quality of a product and also carry out maintenance work on the automatic machines. Electronic and automatic machinery is highly complex and requires a great deal of looking after.

White Collar Electrons

For the most part up to this point, we have seen how electronics is being adapted at a rapidly increasing tempo to the manufacturing end of industry. But electronic servants are providing equal if not more assistance to those handling the office affairs of the business world. White collar workers have a large number of electronic servants to help make their chores less monotonous and more efficient, and to enable them to complete them more quickly. Some of these include computers that can process with great speed all sorts of production, sales, inventory and other business data. In addition, there are others used for filing, sorting and for dictation purposes, such as the dictaphone. One of the newest electronic assistants is a stenciling machine.

A stenciling machine is one of the most important tools in any well-run office. The electronic model that is now available is said to cut stencils faster and much better than others used. By employing a photoelectric scanner and a spark for cutting, photos, line drawings, printed forms, and typed copy may be easily and quickly reproduced. A different but equally helpful electronic servant for office work is now available where quick, mass printings are required. It is called a Multiple-Stylus Electronic Printer and was developed by the Eastman Kodak Company.

This electronic automatic printer consists of two separate units, the printer itself and an electronic computer, both of which are connected by a cable. Basically the machine operates from a coded signal which may be provided by a number of sources—holes in automatically-fed punched cards, film, perforated tapes, and magnetic tape among others. When cards with punched holes are used, a photoelectric unit takes the information which their hole-pattern indicates, changes this into electrical impulses and sends these along to the computer. The electronic "brain" first stores the signals and rearranges them in the correct sequence for printing. The computer then

Photo shows printer unit and electronic console which make up Eastman Kodak's speedy electronic printing apparatus. *Eastman Kodak.*

decodes the signals, translates them into predetermined combinations and sequences for the printing styli.

A single row of seven styli in the printer actuated by signals from the computer does the actual printing. The styli strike carbon paper beneath which is the paper receiving the printed

198

message. Characters are formed automatically from built-up rectangular dots. Heat fixes permanently the carbon impression. The electronic printer may have more than one printing head, each of which is capable of producing 300 to 400 characters per second. Six hundred four-line address labels having 96 characters each can be printed per minute.

The Multiple-Stylus Electronic Printer is said to be particularly effective in handling insurance premium notices, utility bills, addresses on magazine labels and numerous other items. Another potential use is seen for it where high-speed printed communications are desired since it can be operated by remote control. By controlling the versatile abilities of the fast moving electron, engineers are constantly thinking of newer ways to ease the tasks of the often harassed office worker.

The bewildering electronic hook-up that controls the operation of the Multiple Stylus Electronic Printer. *Eastman Kodak.*

Typesetting with a Typewriter

Although not quite in the same category as the electronic printer just described, another device based on the magic of electrons, revealed in the winter of 1953, caused quite a stir in the publishing industry. This machine is called the Photon and offers an electronic method of setting type which should cut the cost and work involved in books and newspapers.

Two French electrical engineers, René A. Higonnet and Louis M. Moyroud invented this electronic typesetter with the support of the Graphic Arts Research Foundation of Cambridge, Massachusetts. The Photon looks like an ordinary streamlined office desk with a built-in typewriter. But there are a few external features which hint at its special nature. The keyboard for example, of the standard electric typewriter which it uses, has a fifth row of keys plus four additional keys. To the right of the typewriter is another small unit containing a series of buttons. All these are connected and set in motion an intricately arranged series of electronic, mechanical, and photographic devices within the typesetting machine.

Photon sets up on negative film a page of printed matter exactly the way it will appear in final form. The negative is

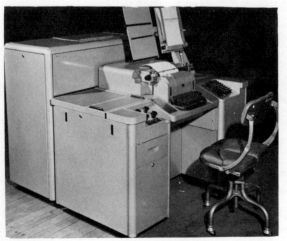

First production unit of the Higonnet - Moyroud, or Photon, photographic type composing machine developed by the Graphic Arts Research Foundation, Inc., and manufactured by its licensee, Photon, Inc.

200

then developed from which the printing plates, either offset or letterpress, are made. Conventional lead typesetting is eliminated. The operator, who need have no special skill other than being able to work a typewriter, starts the electronic composing machine by turning on a switch. Then he selects the line length measure desired, interline spacing, and the proper type family, style and size, using for this purpose the auxiliary control unit at the side. Then he prepares his printer's copy on the typewriter keyboard. As the typist completes each line of type, an electronic "brain" is automatically figuring out how much space must be left between letters and words in order to make the line the right length. If an error is made with a single letter or an entire line, it may be eliminated and typed over.

When a line of typed matter is ready for composing, a bell rings. The operator then presses a button and the machine begins its most important function, the actual composition. The heart of this process is a spinning 8″ glass disc. The disc contains sixteen different and complete alphabets of transparent letters and symbols. As the selected letter speeds by a magnifying lens, a stroboscopic light "stops" the letter's movement and places its image on a roll of photographic film. When a page is set, the film is removed and developed and the reproduction plates made.

The great advantage claimed for this over conventional typesetting equipment is that an operator who had never seen the machine before could be hired one day and be setting type the next, with his speed limited, moreover, only to his or her ability to type. Cutting printing costs is also one of its big assets. The glass scanning disc, for example, which weighs but 24 ounces, and the lens system replaces conventional lead typesetting matrices that would cost $25,000 and weigh almost two tons. The Photon is being produced on a limited scale mainly for the purpose of having the "bugs" removed by actual usage in the publishing field.

Miscellaneous Uses

The applications of electronics in industry and commerce so far mentioned by no means indicate the extent of this fascinating modern development. There are many others which we have not touched such as the sensitive instruments used by chemical, petroleum, and utility companies in working with liquids and gases.

The oscillograph, one of the most outstanding of electronic devices, helps engineers and laboratory technicians determine whether an electrical contrivance is operating properly. By observing the shape of the electronic pattern picked up by the oscillograph screen, a television receiver can be correctly adjusted, an auto's ignition system checked under high-speed conditions, or a radio transmitter's controls accurately set. Karl Braun's laboratory tool, unchanged basically from his original model, has indeed been a great boon for the advancement of our electronic age. Braun's oscillograph was similar in shape to a present-day TV tube. It contained a high vacuum while the inside of the tube's face was coated with a luminescent sub-

The oscillograph, the instrument with the large circular face, being used to check a newly made transistor. *Hydro-Aire Co.*

stance. The cathode-ray beam, striking this inner surface, would trace an electronic pattern of light showing the behavior of the apparatus which the oscillograph was testing.

In Medicine

One of the remarkable characteristics of electronics, as we have probably observed by now, is its enormous versatility. Almost no endeavor of man has not been touched by it and benefited. An excellent example is its contribution to the science of medicine. From the very earliest days of electronic research, many of the instruments and equipment thus developed won recognition as valuable aids in helping man to combat disease. Today doctors and medical scientists rely on a wide assortment of electronic machinery for diagnosis and treatment, as well as for research, in many ailments.

Diathermy machines producing infra-red rays are common electronic appliances used by doctors. Capable of creating heat deep within muscle tissue, infra-red rays reduce muscular pain resulting from strain or other causes. Another kind of apparatus radiates ultra-violet rays, often employed in the treatment of surface skin disorders.

The best-known of all electronic equipment is perhaps still the X-ray machine, discussed earlier. By means of X-ray, a doctor setting a bone fracture can actually see the nature of

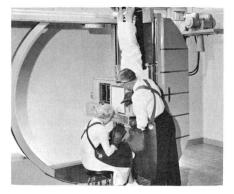

A patient being examined by a fluoroscope with the help of a newly developed X-ray diagnostic table. The table is mounted on an 8-foot ring and can be rotated, instead of being pivoted, into position. It can be turned easily in an arc of 180 degrees. *General Electric Co., X-Ray Division.*

the break and how well he has made the setting. The surgeon, before beginning an operation, can study X-ray pictures of the particular area of the body in which he is interested and make certain in advance that he will meet with no unforeseen problems. Foreign substances such as bullets, shell fragments, or other objects can be located quickly and accurately. Dentists use X-rays for locating decayed or abscessed areas on teeth.

Specialists in the treatment of particular organs of the human body use a modification of the X-ray machine called a fluoroscope for studying the functions and characteristics of those organs. The fluoroscope works almost the same way as an ordinary X-ray unit. It sends X-rays from an electronic apparatus flashing through the body which then strikes a fluorescent screen. A shadow of that portion of the human anatomy under observation falls on the specially coated screen but, unlike an ordinary X-ray photograph, the fluoroscope presents a living image. Thus, a doctor may study the actual beating of the heart, or movements of the stomach and intestines.

The conventional X-ray machine has become far more versatile in its value to the medical world since the early years of its existence. One of its most important jobs today is the detection and treatment of diseases within the human body such as tuberculosis and cancer. As far back as 1898, X-rays were used by doctors to spot the presence of tuberculosis. In combating cancer, X-ray machines serve a dual role. Not only can they detect its presence, but the lethal stream of rays which they

The U. S. Army's new field X-ray unit. Equipment can go to work anywhere, using its own compact power plant. *Picker X-Ray Corporation.*

produce are employed to destroy its malignant cells. Diseased cells are more sensitive to the power of X-rays than healthy cells. But the latter can be seriously harmed if proper care is not taken. Burns and the permanent destruction of healthy cells which in time might be fatal can take place. A person receiving X-ray treatment is protected by careful measurement of the dosage and proper shielding. The shielding is sometimes carried out on the patient or the X-ray tube itself so that it emits only a pencil-thin stream of rays exactly on the area being treated. Ever since science found that X-rays are a potent weapon in the fight against cancer, machines of increasing power have been designed and built for this purpose.

One such giant is a machine capable of producing a 2,000,000-volt stream of X-rays. This unit looks like an artillery siege piece, it is so big, and requires a permanent installation. The X-rays shoot out of the nozzle end in a pencil-thin stream and can be pin-pointed to probe deep within the human body.

Since the conclusion of World War II a still newer colossus among X-ray machines, called a Betatron, has joined the struggle against cancer. Previous to the last world conflict, the Betatron was just being brought to a state of practical usefulness and was employed by physicists in their research work. Out of this activity it was discovered that the enormous X-ray energy which these machines generate, almost ten times greater than the conventional X-ray unit, could be applied to industrial and medical uses. The United States government subsequently became interested in the Betatron when it learned that the machine could X-ray and detect flaws in metal components far thicker than possible with conventional radiograph equipment. Since then the Betatron has also entered the medical field, where it is being used with considerable success in cancer treatment.

The Betatron is an electron accelerator in which these tiny particles of electrical matter are made to move in a circular path at tremendous velocities. This action takes place inside a cir-

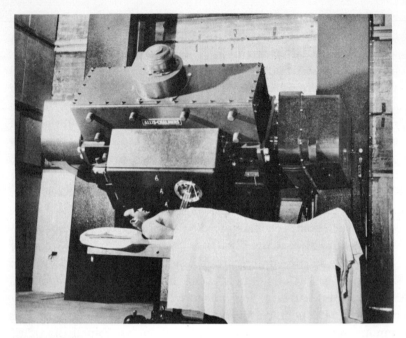

Patient being treated by a multi-million volt medical Betatron machine in the Memorial Hospital, New York City. *Allis-Chalmers.*

cular tube, called a "donut," which contains an extremely high vacuum. While the electrons are spinning on their endless journey inside the tube, a magnetic field located outside the "donut" gives them their accelerating force and also keeps them in their orbit. When they have attained their maximum velocity, on the order of 186,000 miles per second, the electrons are made to strike against a target made of platinum. The result is a stream of X-rays of incredible power. These X-rays are in the form of short quick pulses.

Betatron machines in current use have a range from 2 million to 300 million volts. The latter is primarily used by physicists for research purposes, while those ranging between 22 and 24 million volts are employed in the industrial and medical fields. These have been brought to a high state of development.

One of the latest machines in this field is of a radically new design capable of generating 50,000,000 volts. Called the microwave linear accelerator, this powerful anti-cancer weapon, incorporating many up-to-the-minute developments in radar and atomic physics, weighs 10 tons and shoots electron pulses of tremendous energy onto moving radar waves which travel in a 16' guided path. The electron bursts quickly reach the velocity of light, 186,000 miles per second. This speed, combined with their developed energy, boosts the normal weight of the electrons 100 times. When they reach the end of the radar wave guide, the electron bursts are shot through a thin aluminum window. They have enormous penetrating power and are expected to be effective in attacking cancerous tissue unaffected by other less powerful apparatus.

There are many other electron medical aids, each with its own particular function. The electrocardiograph presents a doctor with a visible pattern of the function of the heart, much the way an oscilloscope produces a visible record of the operation of an inanimate electronic unit. Then there is a machine with the tongue-twisting name of electroencephalograph which helps in the diagnosis of diseases of the brain. Other electronic devices induce artificial shock for certain nervous disorders. Electronic amplifiers are used in hearing aids, and there is an electronic stethoscope. One of the newest instruments in this field is called a sanguinonometer, a device that speeds up the process of blood cell counting. It is expected to play an important role in the atomic age just dawning, since it provides a simple, quick, and accurate mass method of taking blood counts, an important way of detecting the beginnings of radiation sickness among people in the target area of an atomic bomb.

Overexposure to the power of atomic radiation will cause destruction of the blood cells, especially of the red variety which are so vital for good health. When the supply of red blood cells falls below the minimum requirement, anemia, with its pallid complexion, loss of appetite, weakness, and other complications,

207

results. A blood count is employed to check on the condition of the blood. The conventional laboratory method for taking a blood count is slow and tedious, a situation which the newly developed electronic equipment will improve.

The sanguinonometer makes use of a television camera, microscope, and an electronic computer. The TV camera is trained on the viewing sight of the microscope. The image it picks up, the slide with its blood sample, is projected onto a screen. It also does one other thing and that is to send electronic pulses to the computer. These pulses represent blood cells which are detected by the camera's electron beam as it scans the microscope specimen.

The computer not only records these pulses as they arrive from the camera, but it also makes adjustments to allow for the fact that the TV camera beam would view a blood cell more than once. Tests made with this electronic blood cell counter have shown it to be far speedier than a human laboratory technician doing the same job. The instrument can go through a process several times while a technician is completing just one. The sanguinonometer is the work of RCA engineers working with scientists of the Sloan-Kettering Institute.

The Sanguinonometer, a newly developed electronic system for taking quick blood counts. *Radio Corporation of America.*

A West Coast hospital has recently revealed what an operating room of the future will be like as more and more electronic apparatus is adapted for medical purposes. This particular institution specializes in research on brain disorders and is acquiring a surgery room filled with the latest electronic equipment, including devices specially created to measure and photograph weak electrical impulses produced by the brain. Instruments will be available capable of exciting nerve centers deep within the brain. Ultrasonic devices will also be included to assist surgeons, particularly for destroying living cells. In addition, the surgery room will contain X-ray equipment, television cameras, and intercommunication apparatus, as well as special tools for handling radioactive isotopes.

For Scientific Research

Scientific research, no less than practical therapy, is greatly assisted by the magic of electronics, which has given research workers tools of limitless potential with which to investigate the many mysterious realms of science. Two of the most important of these are the electron microscope and the electronic computer.

Scientists connected with the Battelle Memorial Institute are shown here working with the electron microscope. *Battelle Memorial Institute.*

The electron microscope is a product of the technical activity of a number of scientists of many lands, climaxed in the 1930's by the introduction of several different types of these electron magnifiers. In comparison to the optical variety, this electronic research instrument reached a high state of perfection in a remarkably short time—a little more than a decade as measured against the former's several centuries. By the end of 1945 the electron microscope was in wide use in numerous fields of scientific research.

Electron microscopes existing today are of four distinct types: the Emission, Scanning, Shadow and Transmission varieties. The last named is the most successful and therefore the most widely used. This instrument is made up basically of three major units. First there is the electron tube and its various elements, second is the lens system and third an arrangement for transforming the electron image into a visual image.

The electron beam is produced in the usual way in a high vacuum cathode tube. This beam in some instruments is focused on the specimen under observation by electrostatic or electromagnetic fields. After leaving the electron tube, the beam passes through a condenser lens arrangement and finally falls on the specimen being examined. The condenser provides a method to control the intensity of the electron beam and its angular form.

After striking the specimen, electrons pass through it in direct proportion to its thickness and are picked up and highly enlarged by a dual system of lenses. The first of these is called the objective lens and the second the projector. The electrons that have passed through the specimen and have been picked up by the lenses, carry an image of the specimen. This image bearing electronic beam flashes on a fluorescent screen where the electrons are converted into a visual image so the eye can see the enlarged specimen. Very often in place of a fluorescent screen the electron beam is made to fall on a photographic plate so that a permanent picture of the enlargement can be had.

Electron microscopes are far superior to the optical models

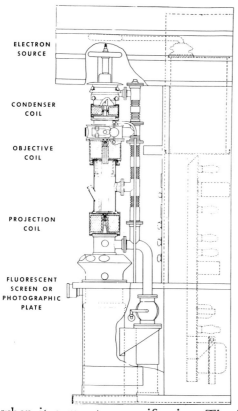

ELECTRON
SOURCE

CONDENSER
COIL

OBJECTIVE
COIL

PROJECTION
COIL

FLUORESCENT
SCREEN OR
PHOTOGRAPHIC
PLATE

Simplified drawing showing the construction of the electron microscope. *Radio Corporation of America.*

when it comes to magnification. The best optical instruments have an enlarging power that ranges somewhere between two thousand and three thousand diameters. The electron types, on the other hand, can go as high as 20,000 diameters. By combining photographic enlargements with the electron microscope, this magnification can be multiplied another fivefold to 100,000 diameters. When this technique is employed, objects whose existence might ordinarily only be surmised can be brought within the range of vision. What this means to the laboratory worker can be easily understood when, for example. a blood corpuscle can be magnified until it is as large as a two-foot sofa pillow; a coin the size of a dime can be made to appear more than a mile in diameter, while a human hair can be blown up to look as big as a giant redwood tree.

Research workers in chemistry, metallurgy, medicine, bacteriolgy, and biology have had many new avenues of investigation opened for them since the electron microscope became a part of their laboratory equipment. Soon they will have a still newer instrument of this kind to aid their research studies called an X-ray microscope. This device is not out of the development state as yet, but when it is available, the instrument will enable laboratory workers to photograph details inside specimens despite their opacity. It will be capable of magnifying up to 1,000 times.

The second of the new electronic tools proving tremendously helpful to those blazing new trails in science is the electronic computer. Since the end of World War II, machines of this nature, both small and large and extremely complex, have been developed to perform incredible feats of calculation with lightning swiftness, fully earning the nickname of "electronic brains."

There are two types of computers. One is called the analogue computer and the other digital. The analogue computer, whose operation is based on physical factors that are similar to mathematical factors, gets its name from the word *analogous,* meaning "corresponding to something else in certain aspects." If we were to pose a particular problem containing physical factors and replace these with certain numerical values, the mathematical processes of the computer could be used to obtain results in numbers that would have a direct relation to the physical factors. For example, "Ohm's Law, one of the fundamental natural laws of electricity, says that 'Voltage equals Current times Resistance.' By substituting different values as currents and resistances, it is possible to perform multiplications with the answers read as voltages."*

---

* *Light on the Future,* International Business Machines Corporation.

Some engineers have likened the speedometer in an auto to a simple type of analogue computer which, incidentally, may also be of a mechanical and electrical nature as well as electronic. With this instrument the rate at which a shaft turns is changed into a value equivalent to the speed of a vehicle. Analogue computers are frequently employed as part of an electronic fire-control system for anti-aircraft and other types of gunnery. They are also much used by research engineers in aeronautics since the computers can simulate a theoretical flight of an airplane or guided missile embodying new design features. In this way ideas can be tested and proved or discarded long before the actual building of the aerial vehicle.

An engineer using an electronic analog computer for the solution of a problem. *Battelle Memorial Institute.*

The digital computer, named for the ten digits of our two hands, is concerned only with the solution of mathematical problems in numerical fashion. It is capable of carrying out automatically extremely long series of steps of involved calculations. In the process of doing this, the computer uses its own particular type of memory as it continuously makes decisions. These machines actually have a long historic background. They are a modern culmination of their mechanical predecessors which go back many centuries to the abacus. One of the first of the digital electronic mental giants was developed by the International Business Machines Corporation and put into use in 1948. Known as the Selective Sequence Electronic Calculator, it has helped scientists and engineers with a wide variety of specialized problems—some involving many millions of sequential calculations. The calculator has also served as a valuable tool to astronomers who have used it to make mathematical computations on the positions of the moon over a period of several hundred years. Further, the computer has helped to plot the courses of the five outer planets. As a result of the electronic brain's assistance, astronomers were able to make corrections in astronomical tables which had been considered standard for many years.

Mainly because of the uses to which this pioneering "brain" had been put, and by studying its operations, IBM engineers were able to design and construct an improved model with twenty-five times the ability of the earlier unit. This high-speed computer is known as the Electronic Data Processing Machine or 701 for short. It is made up of eleven compact and connected units. The Selective Calculator was dismantled to make room for the newer one which is housed in a special room. Its phys-

The 701, IBM's electronic giant computer, is composed of eleven compact and connected units. The calculator is installed in the company's World Headquarters Building in New York City. *International Business Machines Corp.*

ical makeup and operation is typical of many of the superspeed electronic "brains" in existence today.

Among the various units of the 701 are an Electronic Analytical Control Unit, an Electrostatic Storage Unit, a Punched Card Reader, an Alphabetical Printer, a Punched Card Recorder, two Magnetic Tape Readers and Recorders (each of these having two magnetic tapes), a Magnetic Drum Reader and Recorder and, finally, power supply and distribution components. The memory or storage elements of the 701, which are considered the heart of the machine, are made up of all three current types of electronic apparatus such as cathode-ray tubes, magnetic tapes and magnetic drums.

The cathode tubes housed in a special cabinet and known as the Electrostatic Storage Unit are miniature versions of the picture type found in TV sets. They can store the equivalent of

RAYDAC, developed by the Ratheon company, is a giant electronic computer located at the U. S. Navy Air Missile Test Center, California. *Official U. S. Navy Photo.*

20,000 decimal digits on their screens in the form of charged dashes and dots. In a few millionths of a second, any digit stored on the face of the tube can be selected for use. An electronic beam which scans this concentration of digits can read the charges and convert them into electronic pulses. The pulses in turn are interpreted as numbers or calculating instructions.

The magnetic tapes, similar to those used in home sound recorders, are also storehouses for digits. A single reel of magnetic tape can store 2,000,000 digits. These can be read off at the rate of 12,500 digits a second. A roll of tape can be used many times and, if desired, old information can be removed and new data added automatically. A computer may be equipped with a number of magnetic tape storage units.

The third memory unit of the 701 consists of magnetic drums which rotate at a dizzy speed. The surface of these swiftly spinning cylinders is covered with a material that is easily magnetized. Each of these drums can store 40,960 digits which are represented by magnetized spots on the face of the drum. Any of these can be removed for use thousand of times a minute. The memory units just described plus the other components that complete this electronic "brain," perform their lightning swift actions by means of scores of smaller electronic assemblies, miles of wire, 4,000 standard electron tubes and 13,600 germanium diodes.

With superspeed results, the 701 is capable of producing answers to some of the most complex mathematical problems,

International Business Machines Corp.

including partial differential equations and integral equations among others. An illustration of what the abilities of this new giant electronic "brain" can mean to research is evident in the case of an aeronautical engineer pursuing a particular problem involving a wing design. By following a standard mathematical analysis of the problem, 8,000,000 calculating steps would be necessary before results could be obtained. The pattern of this analysis is such that the solution must be arrived at step by step. An engineer working with a desk calculator would require seven years to get his answer. IBM's electronic mental giant can

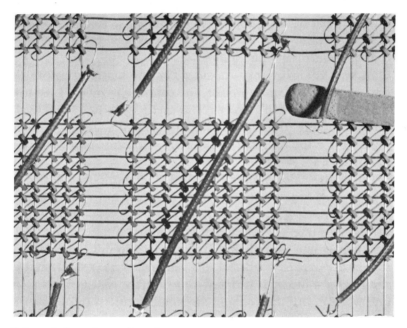

Enlarged view of a section of a new magnetic memory device developed by Dr. Jan A. Rajchman, RCA physicist. Head of a paper match (right) shows relative size of the tiny magnetic cores that store information of the kind used in electronic computers. *Radio Corporation of America.*

do the same job in a matter of minutes. This is the way the 701 goes about solving a mathematical problem.

All the required numbers representing both the digits to be processed, as well as the instructions for the steps to be followed in the calculations, are fed into the computer and automatically flashed to the Electrostatic Storage Unit, the clearing house for all information headed toward and away from all the other units of the "brain." At the very split-second that the computer has acquired all the necessary data for solving the problem, it begins to calculate. It does this with the help of the arithmetic and control circuits within the Analytical Control Unit. This compartment of the "brain" removes numbers from the Storage Unit in keping with initial instructions and carries out any combination of arithmetic operations desired.

By still following instructions given the machine before the start of the calculating process, the control circuit will see to it that all the required steps will be carried out to complete the solution of the problem. Thus, the control system eliminates the need for the operator to interfere with the "brain's" thinking processes.

When the calculation is finished, the results are stored in the Storage Unit. From here, again in accordance with the prior instructions, they will be either printed by a 150-line-a-minute printer at a rate of 1,050 ten-digit numbers a minute, or stored on the magnetic tapes. The "brain" will also put the results on standard punched cards at the rate equal to 2,400 ten-digit numbers a minute. It can add and subtract 16,000 times a second while multiplication and division operations can be carried out at a rate of 2,000 per second.

Aside from its use in the field of aerodynamics, including both aircraft and guided missile research, the 701 is expected to furnish invaluable help to those seeking answers to radiation effects in atomic energy; to compute calculations concerned with new steam and gas turbine designs; and also to help solve problems connected with geophysical matters. Other similar electronic "brains" have been developed to help more accurate weather forecasting methods. The "brain's" ability to digest huge quantities of data and come up with answers within minutes as compared to the hours required by a human mind, can provide weather information long in advance of its arrival.

For Other Problems

In addition to its primary work in the field of science, giant electronic "brains" of the 701 variety are expected to be an important supplement to the army of smaller models now operating in the business world. They will be able to cope with cost accounting and inventory problems on a far larger scale and on a more automatic basis.

Recently, IBM has introduced the 702 which specializes in arithmetic and logic and is designed specifically for business office work. The company claims that it is the fastest and most flexible commercial data processing system ever devised. It is capable of performing more than 10,000,000 operations an hour. The memory tubes, each with a capacity of about all the numbers in the 1,850 pages of the Manhattan telephone directory, feed data to the machine and write answers at the rate of 15,000 letters or numbers a second. The cost of the machine is somewhere about $25,000 so that it will probably be used only by the very largest commercial concerns.

A more imaginative possibility for the use of mammoth electronic computers would be in the field of interplanetary travel. Engineers who have studied this problem believe that electronic "brains" will be vital necessities for the success of such undertakings. Before the first rocket ship could be launched into space, masses of mathematical data would have to be gathered, processed and studied.

There is still another class of electronic "brains" that is capable of doing different kinds of "thinking" chores. For example, one of these developed by the International Business Machines Corporation can translate a limited Russian vocabulary into English. Other machines of this nature, it is said, can be produced that would be able to read books and find desired passages in the text. They may even be given sufficient intelligence to be capable of playing chess. The National Bureau of Standards has developed a "brain" machine of this type called FOSDIC which is a valuable assistant to an electronic computer.

FOSDIC is a high-speed electronic "brain" that can read data from census sheets and then make decisions from the informa-

First ball has set the American Bowling Congress-approved AMF Automatic Pinspotter in motion by hitting the pit cushion, thereby tripping a switch mounted on the back of the cushion. In this picture the ball has already been moved to the ball lift door (lower left corner of pit on this machine), lifted to the return track and sent on its way back to the bowler. *American Machine & Foundry Co.*

tion obtained. It does this by translating certain marks on microfilm copies of census sheets into electrical pulses. These pulses are recorded on magnetic tape. The tape, electronically carrying census data, is then fed into a computing machine. FOSDIC is able to read the equivalent of about sixty document pages a minute.

Up to this moment we have talked about electronics as applied to the more serious fields of man's activities. But the versatility of the tiny electron is by no means confined to these. It has also invaded the home, the world of music, and the field of sports.

It is not difficult, of course, to note the presence of electronic servants in our homes. They light our rooms in the form of fluorescent lamps; cook our foods with the help of infra-red-ray heating units, which at the moment are growing swiftly in popularity, and of course they operate radio and television. In the world of music a great variety of complicated and sensitive electronic equipment is used for recording purposes. More surprising, perhaps, is the actual employment of electrons by instruments for the creation of musical tones and rhythms. Most of us are familiar with the electric organ which can produce beautiful tonal sounds. Now the ranks of musical instruments has witnessed the introduction of an electronic drum, a recent invention. The drum is made to produce its rhythmic beats by means of a leather-covered hammer that is actuated by an electronic circuit. The instrument is said to be capable of developing a higher beat rate than a human drummer while still maintaining the required quality of sound.

The sports field has also found that electronics can heighten the enjoyment of its offerings. One of the really fascinating electronic devices developed for sporting activity is the automatic pinspotter used in bowling. This equipment, which is fully self-operating, can set up tenpins, return the ball and do all the other services now accomplished by a pin-boy. Furthermore, its creators say that it can carry out these things with greater efficiency.

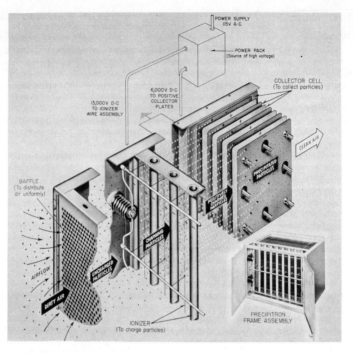

A new low-cost electronic air-cleaning unit, called the PX Precipitron, recently developed by the Westinghouse Electric Corporation. How Precipitron works is shown in this illustration. Particles are dirt, dust, pollen, smoke—some so small they can't be seen by the human eye. *Westinghouse Electric Corporation, Sturtevant Division.*

The pinspotter is basically an electro-mechanical machine, which means that electric circuits control a mechanical system to do the various jobs. The unit stands a little over five feet high and is designed to fit regulation alleys without alterations. The pin-spotter begins to work the minute a ball strikes a switch-equipped cushion in the pits. If a strike is made, a sweeper bar drops quickly to the alley bed. A table comes down and if it finds no pins, reascends briefly. Meanwhile the alley is cleared of deadwood and the table descends again to spot a new set of pins. The deadwood has been pushed into the pit by the sweep bar and onto an endless belt which the machine's makers call the "magic carpet." This unit carries the pins beneath the pit cushion into another conveyor which is wheel-like in shape and called the "pinwheel." This lifts the pins to the top of the machine.

While this action is taking place, the bowling ball is moved to the corner of the pit by the "magic carpet" and raised to a ball return track. This last bit of action is accomplished by an automatic continuous belt-type ball lift. Once placed in the track, the ball returns to the bowler by the force of gravity alone.

When the pins have reached the top of the wheel's rotation, they are released by the pinwheel and positioned bottom-first upon an endless-belt-telescoping distributor. This device places the pins as they are needed in cups fixed to the spotting table. The pins are moved in this manner whether the table is in its normal or respotting position.

One might wonder what happens if the ball does not knock down all the pins. In that case the sweep bar waits until the table descends to lift the standing pins clear of the alley and rises again. After that the sweep bar goes into action and clears away the deadwood. The table lowers once more and replaces only the former standing pins in their exact locations from which they were taken. Precisely replacing pins that have been offspotted by the first ball is considered one of the electronic Pinspotter's most skillful maneuvers.

The electronic robot is equipped with additional devices to make it still more versatile, including a Pinvisor, Pindicator and Radaray Foul Detector. The Pinvisor is a screen affair, or electronic scoreboard, that can be attached to the Pindicator. It tells the bowler whether he has made a strike or if any pins have been left standing. The Pinvisor is also able to show if the first or second ball has been thrown and if a foul has been committed. This information shows up on illuminated glassed-in panels. The Radaray tells the machine when a foul has been committed. This occurs when a beam of light is broken by the bowler as the ball is delivered.

CHAPTER SIX

ELECTRONICS AND THE FUTURE

In the approximately fifty years of its existence, electronics has advanced to peaks of achievement with a speed appropriate to its own way of operation. What does the next half-century of developments in this field hold for our world? In view of the extraordinary accomplishments of the past and present, we can safely let our imaginations wander at will in the answer. Authorities in electronics tell us that what we are witnessing so far merely scratches the surface, compared to what lies in store. A hint of what is to come appears in the projects now at various stages of laboratory development. In some few instances early working models have already emerged from the scientist's workshop.

Future developments in electronics can be roughly divided into two groups, basic technical advances in the science itself, and the adaptation of these advances for practical everyday use. Of the former group there is no question that the most outstanding representative at the moment is the transistor, an invention for which scientists working for the Bell Telephone Laboratories are largely responsible.

The transistor is a midget-size electronic power source that can perform many of the jobs now being done by vacuum tubes and can do them far more efficiently. Little bigger than a kernel of corn, it is usually made from a rarely used metal known as germanium. This metal is classed as a semi-conductor because it combines the properties of a conductor material such as copper and an insulator substance like glass. Since it functions very much like an ordinary vacuum diode tube, the powerful electronic midget is often referred to as a germanium diode.

The transistor has a number of advantages over certain types of vacuum tubes. It has no filament and thus requires no warmup period to begin working. Its power needs are extremely

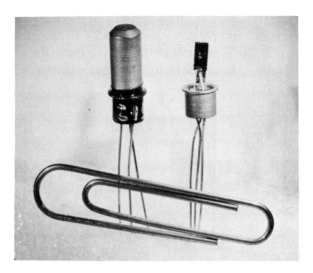

A new type transistor said to out-perform all others now used in military and civilian electronic equipment. Called a Surface-Barrier transistor, it operates at high frequencies and with low power consumption. Photo shows its size in comparison with an ordinary paper clip. On the left is the new transistor hermetically enclosed in its metal case. *Philco Corporation.*

small. A coin wrapped in moistened paper, it is said, can produce enough electricity to make the transistor operate. Despite its tiny size, the electronic power device can amplify electrical signals 100,000 times. In addition to its ability to amplify, the transistor is able to detect and oscillate electric signals as well. It is far more rugged and shockproof than conventional tubes and, therefore, is expected to have a far longer useful life span.

Since its introduction to the field of electronics in 1948, the transistor has been going through progressive stages of development. More than forty different types have been created up to now. However, the two most popular are the point-contact and junction transistors. At first the midget electronic power source was a rather undependable device but diligent work on the part of scientists has brought it to the point where it is as good, and better in many cases, than a wide variety of vacuum tubes. In operation the transistor controls the flow of electrons in a solid much as these moving particles are regulated by the elements in a vacuum tube. In its very brief history to date, the transistor has already begun to replace conventional vacuum tubes in a number of instances.

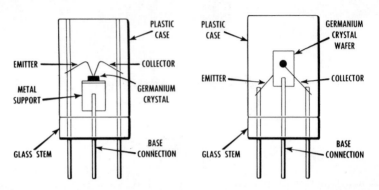

Elements of point-contact type transistor   Elements of junction transistor

Elements of point-contact type and junction type transistors.

Because of its compact size, the transistor has helped to quicken the pace of another technical advance in electronics known as miniaturization. This is also being helped by the use

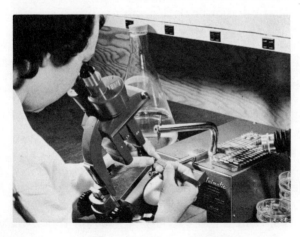

Welding contact "whisker" on basic transistor assembly. Parts are so tiny microscope is needed. *Hydro-Aire Inc.*

of a new method for making wiring circuits which in complex electronic equipment of the kind where compactness is an absolute must, airborne apparatus for one, is a tedious and costly operation. The new technique uses the photo-etcher's process to reduce the size of wiring components as well as to make them cheaper.

One method, as developed by the electronics division of the Boeing Airplane Company, requires a photographic negative to be made from a master wiring diagram of a particular electronic circuit. The negative is placed against a sheet of phenolic plastic, one side of which is coated with a thin copper sheeting. The copper coating is treated with a photo-sensitive acid-resistant enamel called cold top.

The negative and copper-coated plastic sheet are then exposed to brilliant blue arc lights. The dark areas of the negative prevent the light from passing through while the colorless lines of the diagram permit its passage. The light passing through the wiring layout hardens a duplicate pattern on the cold top. Next,

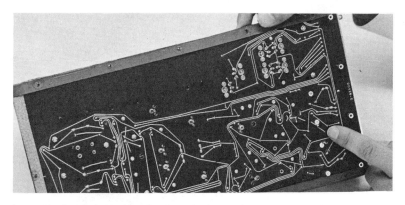

An example of the newly developed electronic wiring technique known as printed circuit. *Boeing Airplane Company.*

the diagram is placed in a pan of developing solution which washes away those areas of the cold top enamel that have not been hardened while under exposure of the arc lights.

A second bath follows consisting of a tankful of ferric chloride solution in which the copper-coated plastic sheet is placed. The liquid dissolves all those parts of the copper sheet not covered by the enamel. The copper portions remaining form an exact duplicate of the master wiring diagram. The copper sheeting has been literally transformed, quickly and accurately, into an intricate wiring layout of thin, hair-like strips.

Aside from the advantages already cited, this method of making wiring circuits is also superior to hand operations in that the wires are held in position much more firmly since the plastic

This is the 50-million-volt "microwave linear accelerator," a radically new type of atom-smasher that is expected to play an important role in the fight against cancer. Three to five feet of concrete protect workers from the penetrating electrons and X-rays produced by this machine. *High Voltage Engineering Corporation.*

backing acts as a support. The photo-etching process, in addition, makes it possible to simplify designs and reduce the number of necessary parts for a particular wiring hook-up. The method lends itself ideally to mass-production techniques since complicated wiring circuits can be duplicated any number of times with great accuracy.

Interesting as these technical electronic advances may be, they are not nearly as fascinating as some of the applications to which electronics is expected to be put in the future. Some of these are a good many years away, but already scientists are preparing the groundwork in laboratories for their eventual practical use. One of the more startling prospects involves electronic controls for motor vehicles. This is the particular dream of Dr. V. K. Zworykin, one of the outstanding electronic scientists in America today.

As a result of up-to-the-minute technical progress with electronic devices, such as the transistor, Dr. Zworykin sees the day when cars and trucks will be rolling along the highways under the complete control of electronic units. The human driver would be just another passenger while the electronic chauffeur guided the car to its destination. Dr. Zworykin is of the opinion that this automatic control system would be particularly valuable for driving on superhighways which is often a very monotonous and mind-dulling chore and also during bad weather conditions. The electronic driving apparatus would include anti-collision features when road vision has been reduced by heavy snow, rain or fog.

If this idea strikes one as being a little too far-fetched, the fact that Dr. Zworykin and his assistants have already demonstrated the basic fundamentals of similar automatic controls in RCA's research laboratory should dispel such feelings. They have used a five-foot model automobile equipped with a storage battery for power and certain electronic control devices to show how the principles of this automatic driving system can be applied. The midget auto can steer itself along an established

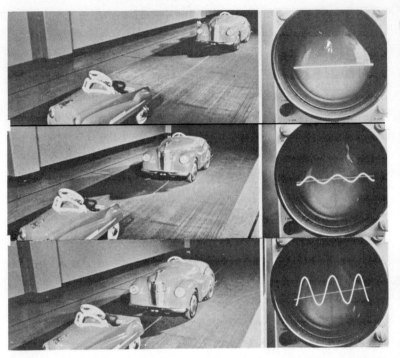

Model car equipped with experimental electronic controls is stopping itself
o prevent collision. *Photo by Joe Covello for* Collier's.

route; stop itself when approaching a metal obstruction and
even turn out of its original path and into a second lane as if to
pass a slower moving car.

The laboratory demonstration set-up includes a cable
stretched out along the floor. The tiny auto straddles and is
guided by the cable which sends out electromagnetic radiations
of a certain frequency. These radiations are picked up by two
coils, one on each side of the steering mechanism at the front
end of the car. Just so long as the coils receive equal amounts of
power from the electro-magnetic signals, the car remains cen-
tered over the cable. However, if either the right or left coil
should get more power than the other then the auto swerves in

either a right or left direction. When this condition aris
equalizing electronic units connected to servo-mechanisn
which supply the power, steer the car back in a straight pat

The anti-collision portion of the equipment is even mo:
amazing. Placed at certain intervals along the cable are ele
trical circuits which send out warning signals—of a differen
frequency from that guiding the car—whenever a movabl
obstruction passes or is stalled over them. The warning signal
radiate from the rear of the moving or stalled obstruction and
have been described by Dr. Zworykin as a "radio tail." Receiv
ing equipment aboard the electronically controlled car picks
up these signals and automatically applies the brakes. The
"radio tail" may stretch as much as 200′ to the rear of the obstruction, and the closer the approaching electronic chauffeur
comes, the stronger will the warning signals be received.

A variation of this can occur on highways with two lanes
going in the same direction. In the laboratory two parallel guidance wires serve as twin highway lanes. These are connected by
diagonal lengths of wire at certain intervals. As the electronic
car at the rear of another senses the obstruction ahead, the electronic equipment sends instructions to its mechanical muscles to
steer the auto into the outer lane and pass the blocking car.

Actually the adoption of automatic electronic controls for
automobiles such as Dr. Zworykin proposes need not be such a
distant event. Cars today are relieving the driver more and more
of many of the chores of operating his vehicle. There are already
available power units that help with the steering and braking
actions. Headlights can be dimmed or made brighter automatically and directional signals turned on and off with little
or no effort on the part of the driver. Automatic transmissions
have reduced necessary shifting chores to the barest minimum.
So the jump to Dr. Zworykin's electronic controls could be a
comparatively short one.

An electronic development whose future application is in the
more immediate realm of usefulness than that of electronic auto

An experimental recording head unit, the heart of the newly developed video tape recorder. *Radio Corporation of America.*

controls, is a method for recording television shows on magnetized tape. This technique of "electronic photography" was brought to a successful stage by scientists of RCA's David Sarnoff Research Center. In addition to its importance to the television field the system is expected to have a powerful impact on the motion picture industry.

Almost everyone is familiar with the use of magnetic tape for the recording of plays, speeches or musical programs. Now, generally the same method has been employed to record visual scenes either in black-and-white or color. This can be done quickly and economically without the conventional need for photographic development or processing for reproduction purposes. The video tape recorder picks up both the sound and picture on a single strip of magnetically coated plastic as thin as paper and one-half inch wide. A single piece of equipment does both the recording and reproduction. Once the tape has accomplished its recording job, it can either be stored for future use

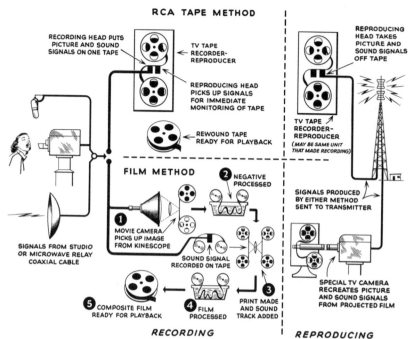

RCA TAPE METHOD

RECORDING HEAD PUTS PICTURE AND SOUND SIGNALS ON ONE TAPE

TV TAPE RECORDER-REPRODUCER

REPRODUCING HEAD PICKS UP SIGNALS FOR IMMEDIATE MONITORING OF TAPE

REWOUND TAPE READY FOR PLAYBACK

REPRODUCING HEAD TAKES PICTURE AND SOUND SIGNALS OFF TAPE

TV TAPE RECORDER-REPRODUCER *(MAY BE SAME UNIT THAT MADE RECORDING)*

FILM METHOD

2 NEGATIVE PROCESSED

1 MOVIE CAMERA PICKS UP IMAGE FROM KINESCOPE

SIGNALS FROM STUDIO OR MICROWAVE RELAY COAXIAL CABLE

SOUND SIGNAL RECORDED ON TAPE

3 PRINT MADE AND SOUND TRACK ADDED

4 FILM PROCESSED

5 COMPOSITE FILM READY FOR PLAYBACK

SIGNALS PRODUCED BY EITHER METHOD SENT TO TRANSMITTER

SPECIAL TV CAMERA RECREATES PICTURE AND SOUND SIGNALS FROM PROJECTED FILM

RECORDING | *REPRODUCING*

Steps in recording and reproducing a television program by RCA video tape method as compared to typical film method used today. *Radio Corporation of America.*

or wiped clean, by an electronic method, and used over and over again for other recording chores. Unlike colored film which requires lengthy and costly processing, the electronic recorder can pick up live scenes and use them instantly.

The TV tape recorder works essentially in this manner. A standard television camera is used to pick up a scene which is then converted in the usual way into electrical impulses for transmission. These electrical signals or impulses are impressed onto the magnetized tape by means of a recording head, a small horseshoe-shaped electromagnet. As the plastic tape is drawn across the recording head, the latter continuously alters the polarity of the magnetic oxide particles on the tape. As a result they become a compact code of the original signal.

To play back the pictorial scene and sound, the tape is drawn across the same or a similar-shaped head. The magnetic code which it carries causes an alternating current to flow in the windings around the reproducing head. This current closely duplicates the original signal.

It was no easy task which the RCA scientists had set themselves in undertaking the development of the video tape recorder. The great stumbling block was to devise a way to capture TV signals that vibrate millions of times a second. Ordinary sound signals go up to 20,000 cycles per second and present no special problem in transfer to magnetized tape. The secret of RCA's success lies in maintaining the speed of the video recording tape at a manageable level as it keeps pace with the frequencies of the TV signals. The specially-developed recording and reproducing heads led to this triumph. In the experimental video tape recorder now existing, the tape speed is thirty feet a second. Those who developed this electronic apparatus are working to reduce that speed still further.

The magnetic tape reels of the present laboratory model are 17″ in diameter and are capable of recording four minutes of a television show. This is another part of the recording equipment that is expected to be made better in the near future so that it can tape fifteen minutes of a particular program. To capture a color TV program, the magnetized tape carries five parallel channels. There is a single recording channel for each of the primary color signals, red, green, and blue; another channel for the synchronizing signal; and a fifth for sound. Black-and-white recordings are less burdensome for the tape, since only two channels are required. One of these is for the picture and synchronizing signals and the other for the sound.

In December, 1953, the video tape recorder gave its first public demonstration. A color television program was sent out from the studios of the National Broadcasting Company in New York City and transmitted via microwave relay to the David Sarnoff Research Center in Princeton, New Jersey, 45 miles away. The

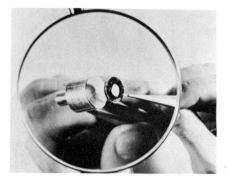

Magnified model of the two basic elements of experimental RCA Atomic Battery, which by means of a new method makes it possible to convert atomic energy directly and simply into small but usable quantities of electrical energy. *Radio Corporation of America.*

program was seen on two color TV receivers for comparative purposes. One of these showed the program direct while the other presented portions of it as picked up and sent out by the tape recorder. Viewers looking at the simultaneous transmission could notice little difference in reception. According to those who are directing the development of this equipment, the video tape recorder is about two years away from commercial use.

Scientists and engineers pushing back the frontiers of electronics have lifted the curtain on still another of their labora-

EXPERIMENTAL RCA ATOMIC BATTERY

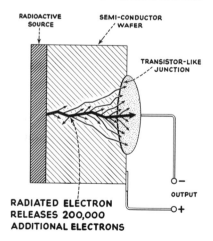

RADIOACTIVE SOURCE

SEMI-CONDUCTOR WAFER

TRANSISTOR-LIKE JUNCTION

OUTPUT

RADIATED ELECTRON RELEASES 200,000 ADDITIONAL ELECTRONS

Simplified cross-section view of experimental RCA Atomic Battery. Radioactive source, which is strontium-90 in present version, radiates billions of electrons (beta particles) per second for many years. Each electron captured by the semiconductor wafer, releases on the average 200,000 more electrons which build up voltage as they flow across the junction. *Radio Corporation of America.*

tory wonders. This one promises for the more distant future to have far-reaching influence on many phases of our living habits. This development is closely tied in with that other current scientific marvel, atomic energy. The device is an atomic battery about the size of a dime. Using a new means for converting nuclear energy into electricity, the midget power source, strictly a laboratory curiosity at the moment, can generate a millionth of a watt of electricity. In a recent demonstration of its ability, the miniature atomic battery supplied current for a transistor which was hooked up to an electronic circuit that produced a high whining whistle heard 20′ away.

This revolutionary atom-electronic device is the brain child of scientists connected with the research laboratory of the Radio Corporation of America. The tiny battery consists of a minute piece of strontium-90 and a wafer thin transistor. Strontium-90 is a radioactive isotope, a by-product that results in large quantities when uranium-235 is bombarded and smashed by neutrons in a reactor. The radioactive substance is fastened to the transistor. Unlike the indirect methods for converting atomic energy into useful energy now being employed, involving complicated arrangements that first change nuclear energy into heat and steam which is then used to operate power-producing devices, the principles applied by the small atomic battery does this in a more direct fashion.

Strontium-90 is an extremely lively source of beta ray particles, which are electrons in super-high-speed motion. The beta rays bombard the silicon wafer transistor. For every electron shooting away from strontium-90, estimated to total several billion a second, 200,000 are released from the silicon wafer. As these slower moving electrons travel across the wafer's junction point, an electric current is produced. Scientists call the electronic activity going on within the transistor an electronic-voltaic effect which is an unusual occurrence of solid-state physics. The practical use of this principle of physics is being pioneered for the first time with this tiny battery.

236

Strontium-90 has a half-life of twenty-years, which means that during that period, a fresh quantity of strontium-90 will have lost one-half of its maximum radioactive energy. A battery incorporating its power, therefore, would still run at half-energy after twenty years.

Some of the first applications seen for this midget battery once it is perfected will be in the communications field for devices like portable radios. It will also bring about vast improvements in hearing aids which depend solely on batteries for their power. It is expected to be of particular value for powering many kinds of airborne electronic equipment where compactness is an absolute must. For the more distant future, individual long-life atomic batteries may provide the power

A solar battery that will convert the energy of the sun directly and efficiently into electricity has been invented at the Bell Telephone Laboratories. Model holds one of the silicon strips in which electronic action takes place during the electrical conversion process. *Bell Telephone Laboratories.*

source needed to run all the electrical apparatus in our homes.

Scientists of the Bell Telephone Laboratories have also developed a new device for generating electric power, utilizing the energy of the sun. Their invention, called a solar battery, uses the sun's rays to create intense electronic activity in thin strips of silicon—about the size of ordinary razor blades—impregnated with particles of boron. The silicon strips, extremely sensitive to light, are linked together electrically. The high-speed action of the released electrons within the silicon strips develops voltage which becomes direct electrical current that can be stored in the battery. The useful electric power produced by the solar battery is estimated to be 50 watts per square yard of surface. Since nothing is consumed or destroyed in the energy conversion process, and with no moving parts, the Bell solar battery should theoretically last forever.

The experimental solar battery is of midget size but even now has sufficient strength to flash radio signals for a distance of several miles. Once perfected, solar batteries are expected to play a useful role in the telephone field. They might serve as a power source for mobile radio telephone equipment, or as sun-powered battery chargers at amplifier stations in rural telephone systems.

In the future, telephone communication is expected to be coupled with television so that people will be able to see as well as talk to one another.

The future also promises to witness far greater use of telephone recordings and talk-back devices, which even now are employed on a limited scale. Thus, if a person should place a call and be unable to get his party, a recording unit will take the message. A play-back device can also deliver a message if one is intended for the original caller. Telephone engineers are also working to develop a tiny wrist radio transmitter-receiver that will allow two-way conversations to any point within a city area while the wearer is walking outdoors. We have seen that one portion of this device, the receiver, has already been developed

238

on a practical basis. Just as soon as electronic experts learn how to miniaturize bulky transmitting equipment still further, the other half of the midget radio, the transmitter, will make its appearance.

New York City even at this moment boasts a restricted service in which the user carries a midget-size receiving unit. By placing this to the ear at a signal, a number assigned the user may be received, indicating that a conventional call is waiting. The individual thereupon goes to a public phone and calls a telephone central bureau where an operator will give him the original message.

Telephone robots will also assist dialing systems of the future by taking a number from a caller, who will give it by voice, and automatically dial it. A robot of this nature called Audrey is already well advanced in development in the United States.

These are just a few of the many wonders of electronics to which we may look forward in the years ahead. They are but a drop in a bucket compared with the ultimate number of bewildering electronic marvels which we can expect. This feeling was expressed perhaps even more vividly by Brigadier General David Sarnoff, head of the Radio Corporation of America, during the dedication ceremonies of the Navy's big Jim Creek radio transmitter. He said, "When we look at this big structure we must remember that while its skeleton is concrete, steel and copper, its heart is the electron—the tiniest thing in the universe. For forty-seven years I have lived with the electron and my experience points to one conclusion: great as the electron's achievements have been, we are still in the horse and buggy era of its development."

INDEX

accelerator, microwave linear, 207
Agtron, 171
aircraft carrier radar landing equipment, 85
aircraft training, electronic, 74
antenna can, 47
antenna reflector, 45
anti-aircraft control, 120
anti-collision radar, 91
A-scope, 48
atomic battery, 236
"audion" electronic tube, 10
Audrey, 239
automatic devices, 195
automatic ground control approach, 81
automatic pilot, 157
automatic pinspotter, 221
aviation electronics, 155

Babcock, Clifford, 11
battery, atomic, 236
battery, solar, 238
Beam rider, 118
Betatron, 205
"blip," 49
Bohr, Niels, 12
Branly, Edouard, 8
Braun, Karl F., 3, 6, 19, 31, 32
Breit, Gregory, 36

canned foods, 172
Carnegie Institution, 36
cathode rays, 3

cathode-ray tubes, 3, 19
cellophane plastics, 178
closed-circuit television, 182
Command System, 117
coherer, 8, 9
Coolidge, Dr. William D., 22
Crookes, Sir William, 3, 5, 12, 19, 31, 32
Cyclotron, 24

De Forest, Lee, 8, 9, 11, 18
Desk Fax, 139
diathermy machines, 203
dielectric heating, 193
DME, 77

Echograph, 99
"Edison Effect," 6, 7, 8, 9, 10, 16
Edison, Thomas, 6, 16, 31
electrocardiograph, 207
electroencephalograph, 207
electromagnetic waves, 25
electron gun, 20
electron microscope, 210
electrons, 11
    in medicine, 203
    white collar, 197
electronic aircraft training, 74
electronic calculator, selective sequence, 214
electronic computer, 212
electronic controls for motor vehicles, 229
electronic drum, 221
electronic life boat, 113

electronic log, 160
electronic microscope, 21
electronic nutcracker, 173
"electronic photography," 232
Electronic Printer, Multiple-Stylus, 198, 199
electronic stenciling machine, 197
electronic tube, "audion," 10
electronic tubes, 16
electronic weather recorders, 104
electronics and the future, 224
electronics, aviation, 155
electronics for metal products, 175
electronics for scientific research, 209
electronics for travel, 155
electronics, historical development, 1
electronics in communications, 139
electronics, marine, 165
electronics, railroad, 163
Excitron, 24

fischlupe, 98
fishing by radar, 97
Fleming, Sir Ambrose, 8, 9, 16
Fleming valve, 9, 10
flight simulators, 107
food inspection and preparation, 171
foods, canned, 172
FOSDIC, 220

GCA, 81, 157
Geiger counter, 178
Geissler, Heinrich, 3, 19
Ground Control Approach system, GCA, 62

ground training for pilots, 106
guided missiles, 116
gyroscopic-pilots, 166

H system, 61
hearing aids, 207
heating, dielectric heating, 193
heating, induction, 194
heating processes, 192
Homing Guidance, 119
Hertz, Heinrich, 31, 32, 34

IFF, 61
induction heating, 194
infra-red ray fluorescent lamps, 221
infra-red ray, 192, 203
Ignitron, 24
instrument trainer, 111

Jim Creek radio transmitter, 141

Klystron, 24

long-waves, 141
Loran, 166, 167

magnetic tape, 232
Magnetron, 24, 44
Marconi, Guglielmo, 33, 34, 35
marine electronics, 165
marine radar, 92
Maxwell, James Clerk, 25, 32
microwave linear accelerator, 207
microwaves for communications, 133
miniaturization, 226
Multiple-Stylus Electronic Printer, 198, 199

"Navascreen," 76
Navigation System, 120
Nike, 118

oboe arrangement, 60
ocean-liner radar, 95
oscillograph, 21, 202

photoelectric tubes, 25, 180
Photon, 200
picket patrol planes, 73
Pindicator, 223
"pip," 49
pinspotter, automatic, 221
Pinvisor, 223
Powergraph Position Tracker, 92
PPI-scope, 48
printing wiring circuits, 227
proximity fuse, 64
radar, 21
    aircraft carrier landing equipment, 85
    anti-collision, 91
    beacon, 77
        buoy, 93
    bombsights, 70
    electronic gunsight, 69
    equipment, railroad, 99
    infantry, 73
    installations, automatic, 72
    jamming, 66
    marine, 92
    marker buoy, 94
    military, 69
    to the moon, 87
    ocean-liner, 95
    operation, 41
    origin, 31
    peacetime, 87
    range finder, 62

sentry, 100
tornado warning equipment, 102
trainer, 76
World War II, 53
Radaray Foul Detector, 223
radiation laboratory, 39
radio beacons, 166
radio telephone, two-way, 131
radio transmitter, Jim Creek, 141
radiophoto, 139
railroad electronics, 163
railroad radar equipment, 99
ramark, 93
RAWIN, 123
reading weather conditions, 123
reflector, antenna, 45
Reservisor, 161
rescue devices, 111
Resnatron, 24
Resotron, 176, 250
Roentgen, Doctor Wilhelm, 3, 5

sanguinonometer, 207
SARAH, 111, 112
Selective Sequence Electronic Calculator, 214
sentry radar, 100
701, the, 214, 216
702, the, 219
Shoran system, 61
"simplane," 75
simulators, flight, 107
"Skysweeper," 120
solar battery, 238
Somascope, 105
sonar, 29
sound waves in industry, 194
Stoney, G. Johnstone, 3
"sweep," 49

Taylor, Dr. Albert Hoyt, 35, 36, 37
telephone, the, 125
telephone robots, 239
television, 21, 143
  closed-circuit, 182
  color, 151
  without entertainment, 115
Tesla, Nikola, 33, 34
Thales of Miletus, 1
Thomas, Sir Joseph J., 2, 5, 12, 31
Thyratron, 24
tornado radar warning equipment, 102
transistor, 224
Translator, 127
Tuve, Merle A., 36
TV—Eye, 184
two-way radio telephone, 131
typesetting with a typewriter, 200

ultrasonics, 29, 194

"Volscan," 85

Watcher, the, 163
weather conditions, reading, 123
weather recorders, electronic, 104
whaling by radar, 97
white collar electrons, 197
wrist-radio, the, 122

X-ray machine, 203
X-ray tube, 22
X-rays, 28, 175

Young, Leo C., 35

Zworykin, Dr. Vladimir K., 21, 229